pocket guide to HANDGUNS

identification and values

1900 to present

Russell Quertermous

Steve Quertermous

COLLECTOR BOOKS
A Division of Schroeder Publishing Co., Inc.

The current values in this book should be used only as guide. They are not intended to set prices, which vary from one section of the country to another. Auction prices as well as dealer prices vary greatly and are affected by condition as well as demand. Neither the Author nor the Publisher assumes responsibility for any losses that might be incurred as a result of consulting this guide.

Additional copies of this book may be ordered from:

COLLECTOR BOOKS
P.O. Box 3009
Paducah, KY 42002-3009

@9.95. Add $2.00 for postage and handling.

Introduction

This is an identification and value guide. Very little in the way of instruction and directions should be required to use a value guide but some words of explanation might be in order.

First of all the suggested values are just that. They are not the final word on an item's absolute worth. That figure can only be determined by the buyer's willingness to purchase and the seller's ability to hold to an asking price. But the values found in this book should be a reasonable guide of what certain firearms are selling for on average around the country.

Geography plays an important part in establishing value. Some guns are more in demand in particular locales than other firearms that are equal in rarity, workmanship and quantities. There are also guns that have a good resale value just because they are manufactured by a particular company. Maybe the company's track record for producing high quality firearms is especially high. Or, maybe there is just an aura of greatness that has been associated with the manufacturer for one reason or another.

Condition is also of the utmost importance in establishing a value. The values in this guide relate to firearms in very good to excellent condition. That is: in good working condition with no appreciable wear on working surfaces, no corrosion or pitting with only minor surface dents or scratches at one end of the spectrum to: in new condition, used very little with no noticeable marring of the wood or metal with perfect bluing except at the muzzle or on sharp edges.

The value range should be a reasonable guide to the gun's real selling worth. But readers who disagree with the pricing structure are encouraged to do further research to ascertain what they consider to be the value.

The illustrations in this guide are from gun companies' promotional materials and as such are not meant to be representative of size relation.

There is no way that a book of this size can be all inclusive of the firearms made in the world but we hope it is a good survey of most of the firearms that are readily available on the open market.

Contents

Section I
Single Shot

Section II
Revolvers

Section III
Semi-automatics

Acknowledgments

The companies included for the use of catalogs, advertisements and promotional material.

A special thanks to the following gun manufacturers for additional photos, information and assistance: Beretta Arms Co., Inc., Browning, Charter Arms Corp., Colt Industries, Firearms Division, Harrington & Richardson, Inc., Heckler & Koch, Interarms for material on Walther, Star, and Astra handguns, Iver Johnson Arms, Inc., Remington, Smith & Wesson, and Sterling Arms Corp.

Petersen Publishing Company for the use of photographs from *Guns and Ammo Annual* 1977, 1982 and *Hunting Annual* 1983.

Stackpole Books for the use of photographs from W.H.B. Smith's *Book of Rifles.*

Russell Scheffer of Scheffer Studio for graphic arrangement of the material. Russell is always there, day or night, to crank out an amazing amount of work at extremely short notice.

The crew that makes up the editorial staff of Collector Books. Their dedication and hard work make an unbelievable number of books on antiques and collectibles indispensible tools for collectors everywhere.

Section I

Single Shot

American

American Two Barrel Derringer

American 2 Barrel Derringer, Model 1
Caliber: 22 short, long, long rifle; 22 WMR, 38 Special; many other calibers introduced in the early 1980's
Action: Single action; exposed hammer; spur trigger; tip-up barrels
Cylinder: None; cartridges chamber in barrels; 2-shot capacity
Barrel: 3" double barrel (superposed)
Finish: Stainless steel; checkered plastic grips
Estimated Value: $130.00 - $300.00

Colt

Colt Camp Perry

Colt Camp Perry (1st Issue)
Caliber: 22 short, long, long rifle
Action: Single
Cylinder: 1-shot; swing-out flat steel block instead of cylinder with rod ejector
Barrel: 10"
Finish: Blued; checkered walnut grips; built on Officers Model frame
Estimated Value: $640.00 - $800.00

Colt Camp Perry (2nd Issue)
Same as 1st Issue except: 8" barrel (heavier); shorter hammer fall; chambers are recessed for cartridge heads
Estimated Value: $680.00 - $850.00

Fiala

Fiala Single Shot Magazine Pistol
Caliber: 22 short, long, long rifle
Action: Hand operated; slide action to chamber cartridge, cock striker & eject empty case
Magazine: 10-shot clip
Barrel: 3", 7½", 20"
Finish: Blued; plain wood grips; a rare American pistol which had the appearance of an automatic pistol. A shoulder stock was supplied for use with the 20" barrel.
Estimated Value:

Pistol with 3", 7½" barrel	Pistol with all 3 barrels & shoulder stock
$300.00 - $400.00	$650.00 - $800.00

Fiala Single Shot Magazine Pistol

Great Western

Great Western Double Barrel Derringer
Caliber: 38 Special
Action: Single, double barrel; tip up to eject & load
Cylinder: None; barrels chambered for cartridges
Barrel: Superposed 3" double
Finish: Blued; checkered plastic grips; replica of the Remington Double Derringer
Estimated Value: $100.00 - $140.00

Great Western Double Barrel Derringer

Hartford

Hartford Single Shot
Caliber: 22 long rifle
Action: Single action, hand operated, concealed hammer
Magazine: None
Barrel: 6¾"
Finish: Matte finish on slide & frame; blued barrel; black rubber or walnut grips
Estimated Value: $355.00 - $450.00

Harrington & Richardson

H&R USRA Single Shot

H & R USRA Single Shot
Caliber: 22 short, long, long rifle
Action: Single or double; small hinged frame; top break
Barrel: 7", 8", or 10"
Finish: Blued; checkered square butt walnut grips
Estimated Value: $120.00 - $145.00

High Standard

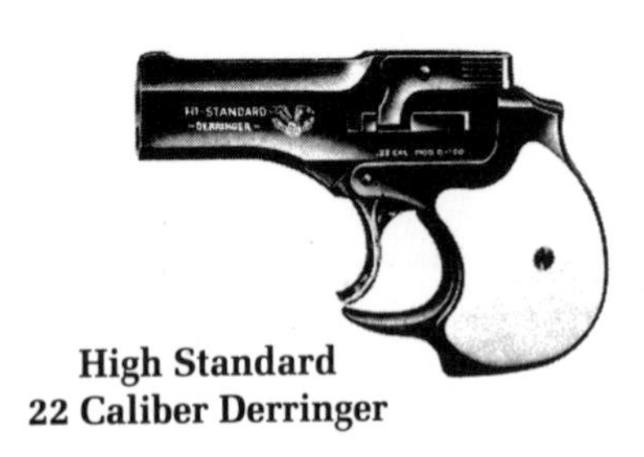

High Standard
22 Caliber Derringer

High Standard Derringer
Caliber: 22 short, long, long rifle; 22 magnum
Action: Double; concealed hammer; hammer block safety; front of trigger guard cut away
Cylinder: None; 2-shot chambers in barrels
Barrel: 3½" double barrel (superposed); dual ejection; cartridge chamber in each barrel
Finish: Blued, nickel or electroless nickel; plastic or walnut grips; gold plated presentation models in walnut case (1965 & 1966); steel barrels; aluminum alloy frame

Estimated Value:

Blued - $100.00 - $125.00
Nickel - $105.00 - $130.00
Electroless Nickel - $120.00 - $150.00
Gold presentation models with case, in unused condition: (with consecutive numbers)
1-derringer $225.00
2-derringer $475.00

Remington

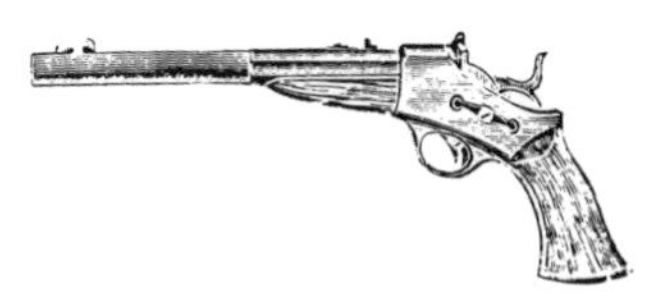

Remington Model 1891, Single-Shot Target

Remington 41 Caliber Double Derringer

Remington Model 1891, Single-Shot Target

Caliber: 22, 25, 32RF, 32 S&W CF
Action: Single
Cylinder: None; single-shot with rolling breech block
Barrel: 8", 10", 12"; half-octagon
Finish: Blued barrel; case-hardened frame; oil finished walnut grips & fore-end; less than 200 made
Estimated Value: $900.00 - $1,200.00

Remington Model 1901, De-Luxe (S-S) Target

Caliber: 22 short, long, long rifle, 44 Russian CF
Action: Single
Cylinder: None; single-shot with rolling breech block
Barrel: 9" round; 10" half-octagon
Finish: Blued; checkered walnut grips & fore-end; approximately 1,000 produced
Estimated Value: $800.00 - $1,000.00

Remington 41 Caliber Double Derringer

Caliber: 41 caliber rim fire
Action: Single; exposed hammer with safety position; sheathed trigger; manual extractor
Cylinder: None; 2-shot double barrel
Barrel: 3" superposed double barrel; ribbed top barrel; barrels swing up to load & extract cartridges
Finish: Blued or nickel; plain or engraved, round butt grips made of metal, walnut, rosewood, hard rubber, ivory, or pearl; serial numbers were repeated on these pistols, so the best way to estimate the age of a pistol is by the markings; marked as follows:

1866-1869: no extractors; left side of barrel E. REMINGTON & SONS, ILION, N.Y.; right side of barrel ELLIOT'S PATENT DEC. 12, 1865

1869-1880: left side of barrel - ELLIOT'S PATENT DEC. 12 1865; right side of barrel - E. REMINGTON & SONS, ILION, N.Y.

1880-1888: barrel rib top - E. REMINGTON & SONS, ILION N.Y. ELLIOT'S PATENT DEC. 12th 1865

1888-1910: barrel rib top - REMINGTON ARMS CO. ILION N.Y.

1910-1935: barrel rib top - REMINGTON ARMS U.M.C. CO. ILION, N.Y.

In 1934 the Double Derringer was called Model No. 95.

Estimated Values:

Plain models	**$500.00 - $1,000.00**
Presentation	**$600.00 - $1,400.00**

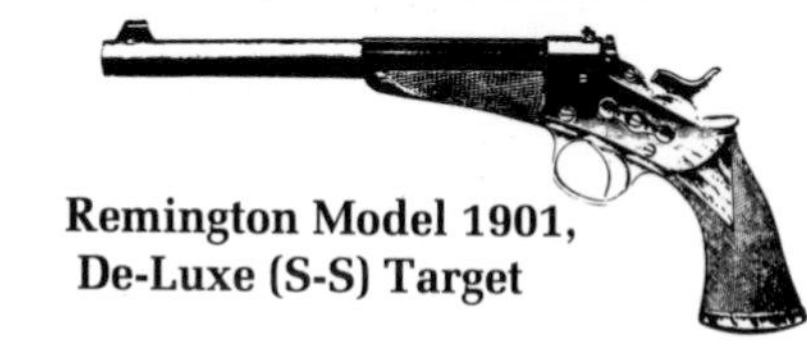

Remington Model 1901, De-Luxe (S-S) Target

Single Shot

Remington Model XP-100 Long Range

Remington Model XP-100 Silhouette

Remington Model XP-100 Long Range
Caliber: 221 Remington "Fire Ball"
Action: Bolt action; single shot; thumb safety
Cylinder: None
Barrel: 10½" round steel with ventilated rib
Finish: Blued with bright polished bolt & handle; brown checkered nylon (Zytel) one-piece grip & fore-end. Fore-end has cavity for adding balance weights
Estimated Value: $220.00 - $275.00

Remington Model XP-100 Silhouette
Similar to the Model XP-100 except: 14½" plain barrel; 7mm Rem. or 35 Rem. calibers; add 4% for 35 caliber
Estimated Value: $255.00 - $320.00

Remington Model XP-100 Varmint Special
Similar to the XP-100 Silhouette except: 223 Rem. caliber only
Estimated Value: $250.00 - $315.00

Ruger

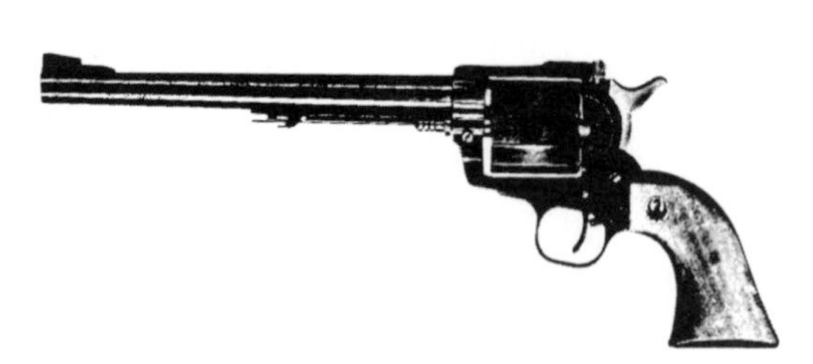

Ruger Hawkeye Single Shot

Ruger Blackhawk Single Shot (Hawkeye)
Caliber: 256 magnum
Action: Single; single shot
Cylinder: None; rotating breech block
Barrel: 8½"; chamber in barrel; under barrel ejector rod
Finish: Blued; smooth walnut grips; built on the Ruger 44 magnum frame & resembles a revolver in appearance
Estimated Value: $750.00 - $950.00

Savage

Savage Model 101 Single Shot
Caliber: 22 short, long, or long rifle
Action: Single
Cylinder: None; single shot; the false cylinder is the chamber part of the barrel
Barrel: 5½" alloy steel; swings out to load; ejector rod under barrel
Finish: Blued barrel; painted one-piece aluminum alloy frame; compressed impregnated wood grips; a single shot pistol built to resemble a single action revolver
Estimated Value: $110.00 - $140.00

Savage Model 101 Single Shot

Sheridan

Sheridan Knockabout
Caliber: 22 short, long, or long rifle
Action: Single; exposed hammer
Magazine: None; single shot
Barrel: 5½"; tip up barrel
Finish: Blued; checkered plastic grips; a single shot pistol that resembles an automatic pistol
Estimated Value: $110.00 - $140.00

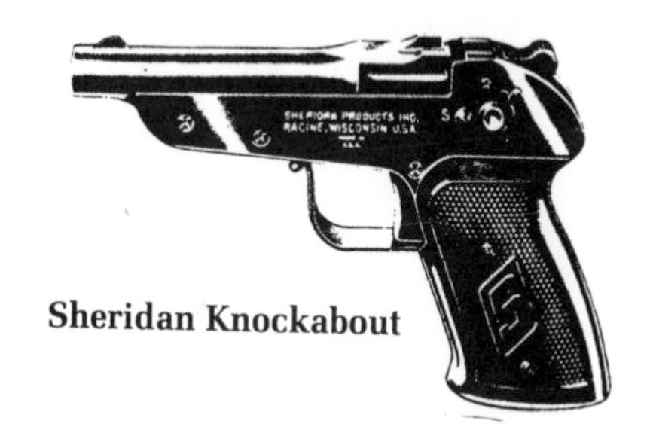

Sheridan Knockabout

Smith & Wesson

Smith & Wesson 1891
Single Shot Target
Caliber: 22 short, long, long rifle
Action: Single; exposed hammer; hinged frame (top break); single shot
Cylinder: None
Barrel: 10"
Finish: Blued; hard rubber square butt grips
Estimated Value: $285.00 - $370.00

Smith & Wesson 1891
Single Shot Target Pistol

Single Shot

Smith & Wesson
Perfected Single Shot
Similar to Model 1891 Single Shot except: double & single action; checkered square butt walnut grips; the U.S. Olympic team of 1920 used this pistol; therefore, it is sometimes designated "Olympic Model." Add $125.00 for Olympic Models
Estimated Value: $330.00 - $420.00

Smith & Wesson Straightline

Smith & Wesson Straightline
Caliber: 22 short, long, long rifle
Action: Single; exposed striker (hammer); single shot
Magazine: None
Barrel: 10"; cartridge chamber in barrel; barrel pivots to left to eject & load
Finish: Blued; walnut grips; pistol resembles automatic pistol ; sold with metal case, screwdriver & cleaning rod; add $150.00 for gun with original case & accessories
Estimated Value: $800.00 - $1,000.00

Sterling

Sterling Model X Caliber

Sterling Model X Caliber
Caliber: 22 short, long, long rifle; 22 magnum, 357 magnum, 44 magnum.
Action: Single action; single shot
Magazine: None
Barrel: 8" or 20" heavy octagonal; a caliber change is made by changing barrel
Finish: Blued; smooth wood, finger-grooved grips & small lipped forend; a silhouette-style single shot pistol with interchangeable barrels for caliber change; add 50% for additional barrel
Estimated Value: $140.00 - $175.00

Stevens

Stevens Tip-Up Pocket
Caliber: 22 short or 30 RF
Action: Single; sheath trigger
Cylinder: None; single shot with tip-up barrel
Barrel: 3½"; part octagon
Finish: Blued barrel with nickel plated frame and all blued; walnut square butt grips; Marked "J Stevens A. & T. Co."
Estimated Value: $160.00 - $200.00

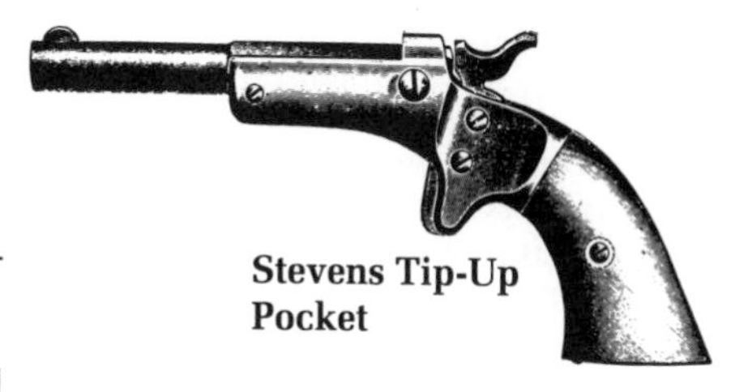

Stevens Tip-Up Pocket

Stevens Hunter's Pet
Caliber: 22 long rifle, 25 RF, 32 RF, 38 long RF, 44 long RF, 38-40, 44-40, 38-35, 44-50, or 24 gauge
Action: Single; sheath trigger
Cylinder: None; single shot with pivoting barrel
Barrel: 18", 20", 22", or 24" octagon & half octagon
Finish: Blued barrel; nickel plated frame & detachable skeleton stock; smooth, walnut, square butt grips
Estimated Value: $350.00 - $450.00

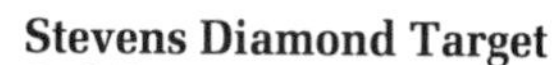

Stevens Diamond Target
Caliber: 22 RF long rifle (black powder 1888 to 1912); 22 long rifle (smokeless powder)
Action: Single; sheath trigger
Cylinder: None; single shot with tip-up
Barrel: 6", 10"; part octagon
Finish: Blued barrel & nickel plated frame to 1912; all blued after 1912; Marked "J. Stevens A. & T. Co.;" walnut square butt grips
Estimated Value: $170.00 - $225.00

Stevens Diamond Target

Stevens Lord Gallery
Caliber: 22 long rifle, 25 RF (smokeless powder)
Action: Single; tip-up barrel
Magazine: None; single shot
Barrel: 6", 8", or 10"; octagon breech
Finish: Blued barrel; plated frame; walnut grips with butt cap; blued frame after 1912; Marked "J Stevens A. & T. Co."
Estimated Value: $180.00 - $235.00

Stevens Lord Gallery

Single Shot

Stevens "Off-Hand" 1907-1915
Caliber: 22 long rifle, 25 RF (smokeless powder)
Action: Single; tip-up barrel
Cylinder: None; single shot
Barrel: Octagon breech; 6", 8", or 10"
Finish: Blued barrel; plated frame; walnut grips with butt cap; blued frame after 1912; Marked "J. Stevens A. & T. Co."
Estimated Value: $220.00 - $275.00

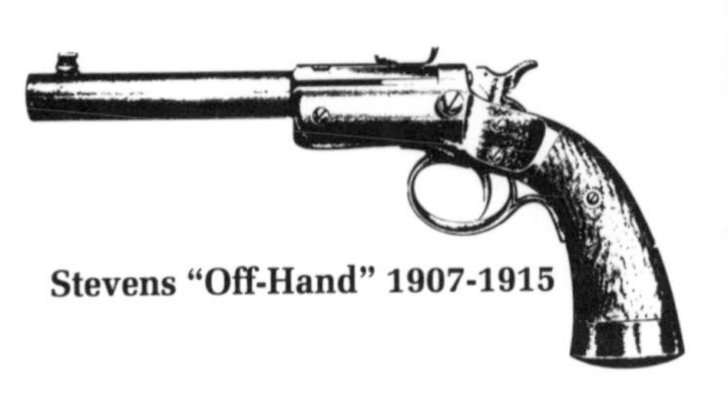

Stevens "Off-Hand" 1907-1915

Stevens Off-Hand 1923-1939
Caliber: 22 long rifle
Action: Single; tip-up barrel
Cylinder: None; single shot
Barrel: Octagon breech; 6", 8", 20", or 12¼"
Finish: Blued barrel & frame, also plated frame; walnut grips with butt cap
Estimated Value: $210.00 - $270.00

Stevens Single-Shot Target

Stevens Off-Hand 410
Caliber: 410 gauge (2½" chamber)
Action: Single; tip-up barrel
Cylinder: None; single shot
Barrel: Octagon breech; choked 8" or 12¼" barrel
Finish: Blued barrel & frame, also plated frame; walnut grips with butt cap; Marked "J Stevens Arms Company."
Estimated Value: $200.00 - $260.00

Stevens Single-Shot Target
Caliber: 22 long rifle
Action: Single; tip up barrel; round knurled cocking piece
Cylinder: None; single shot
Barrel: Round, 8"
Finish: Blued (blackish blue color); black composition checkered grips; a single shot target pistol with the configuration of an automatic pistol; marked "J. Stevens Arms Company."
Estimated Value: $220.00 - $275.00

Stevens Off-Hand 410

Thompson Center

Thompson Center Contender
Caliber: 22 long rifle to 45-70 Gov't.; over the years approximately 35 to 40 calibers were made including some wildcat calibers. It is presently made in 18 calibers: 22 long rifle, 22 Win. mag., 22 Hornet, 222 Rem., 223 Rem., 270 Rem., 7mm TCU, 7x30 Waters, 30-30 Win., 32-20 Win., 357 mag., 357 Rem. maximum, 35 Rem., 10mm auto, 44 mag., 445 Super mag., 45-70 Gov't., 45 Colt/410 gauge
Action: Single action with adjustable trigger; the frame will accommodate any caliber barrel, & the hammer adjusts to rim fire or center fire ammunition.
Cylinder: None, single shot
Barrel: 8¾" (discontinued in the early 1980's), 10" 14" (introduced in the late 1970's), 16¼" (introduced in 1990). In octagon or round; regular or bull barrel; plain or ventilated rib; the 45 Colt/410 gauge barrel has a removable internal choke to use for 410 gauge shot shells
Finish: Blued; checkered or plain walnut grip & fore-end; add 6% for internal choke & ventilated rib; add 4% for 16" barrel
Estimated Value: $245.00 - $300.00

Thompson Center Contender

Thompson Center Contender Armour Alloy II
Similar to the Contender except the parts & barrels are not interchangeable with the standard model Contender. It has a special Armour Alloy II non-glare satin finish. Made in the following calibers: 22 long rifle, 223 Rem., 357 magnum, 357 Rem. maximum, 44 magnum, 7mm TCU, 7x30 Waters, 30-30 Win., 35 Rem., 45 Colt/410 gauge. The 45 Colt/410 gauge has a removable internal choke to use with regular 410 gauge shot shells in 10" bull barrel or ventilated rib barrel. All other calibers use 10" bull barrel or 14" bull barrel; add 5% for ventilated rib with internal choke; add 3% for 14" barrel
Estimated Value: $240.00 - $300.00

Thompson Center Contender Hunter
Caliber: 223 Rem., 7x30 Waters, 30-30 Win., 357 Rem. maximum, 35 Rem., 44 magnum, 45-70 Gov't.
Action: Single action; adjustable trigger
Cylinder: None, single shot
Barrel: 12" or 14" round with T/C Muzzle Tamer to reduce muzzle jump & recoil
Finish: Blued; smooth walnut grip with rubber insert in rear to cushion recoil; smooth walnut fore-end; sling swivel studs, QD swivels & nylon sling; add $10.00 for 14" barrel
Estimated Value: $410.00 - $515.00

Webley

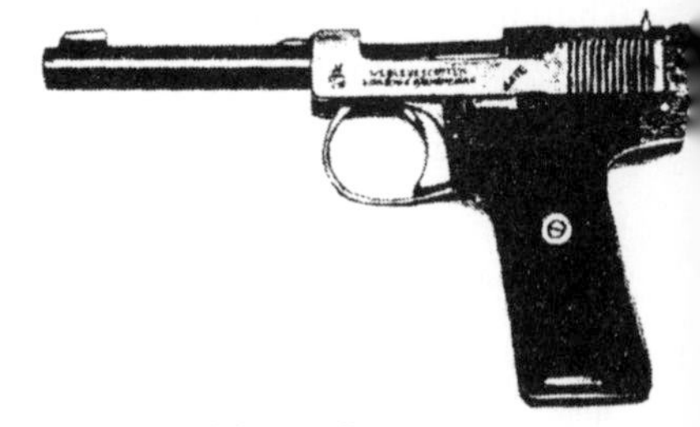

Webley & Scott 1911

Webley & Scott 1911 Model Single Shot
Caliber: 22 short, long, long rifle
Action: Manually operated slide to chamber cartridge; exposed hammer
Magazine: None; single shot
Barrel: 4½" or 9"
Finish: Blued; checkered hard rubber grips
Estimated Value: $300.00 - $400.00

Webley & Scott Match Invader Single Shot Target
Similar to 1909 Model Single Shot Target except: also in caliber 32 S&W long, 38S&W or 38 Special; approximate wt. is 33 oz. Made from about 1952 to 1965.
Estimated Value: $150.00 - $200.00

Weblely & Scott Match Invader

Section II

Revolvers

Astra

Astra 357 Magnum Revolver

Astra Model 357
Caliber: 357 magnum, 38 special
Action: Double action
Cylinder: 6-shot, swing out
Barrel: 3", 4", 6", 8½" heavyweight with rib
Finish: Blued; checkered walnut grips; stainless steel available after 1982 (add 10%)
Estimated Value: $200.00 - $250.00

Astra Model 41, 44
Similar to the Model 357 except 41 magnum or 44 magnum caliber; 6" or 8½" barrel; introduced in the early 1980's; add $10.00 for 8½" barrel; Model 41 discontinued in mid 1980's
Estimated Value: $270.00 - $335.00

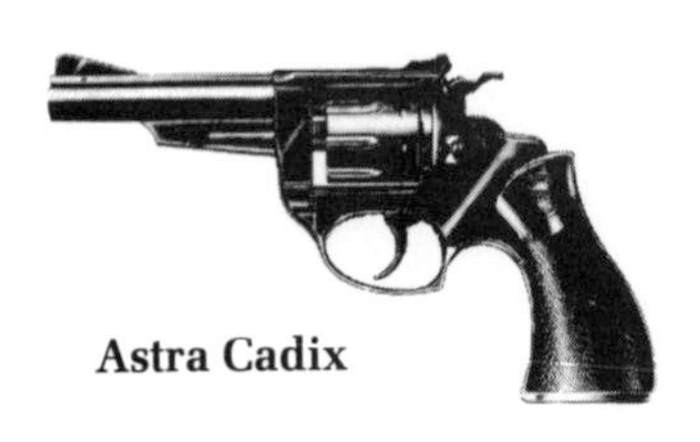

Astra Cadix

Astra Model 45
Similar to the Model 357 except 45 Colt or 45 ACP caliber; 6" barrel
Estimated Value: $210.00 - $260.00

Astra Cadix
Caliber: 22 short, long and long rifle, 38 Special
Action: Double action
Cylinder: Swing out 9-shot in 22 caliber; 5-shot in 38 Special
Barrel: 2", 4", and 6"
Finish: Blued; checkered grips
Estimated Value: $110.00 - $140.00

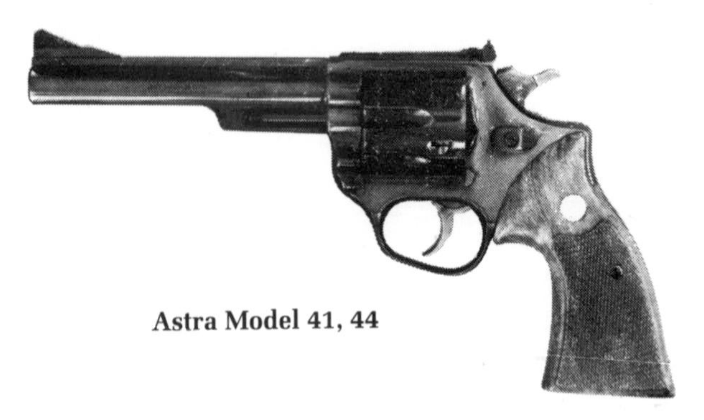

Astra Model 41, 44

Charter Arms

Charter Arms Bulldog
Caliber: 44 Special, 357 magnum (357 magnum discontinued in mid 1980's)
Action: Single and double action; exposed regular or bobbed hammer
Cylinder: 5-shot swing-out
Barrel: 2½", 3", 4", 6" (4" & 6" discontinued in 1985)
Finish: Blued or stainless steel; oil finished, checkered walnut bulldog grips or Neoprene grips; add 20% for stainless steel model
Estimated Value: $160.00 - $200.00

Charter Arms Bulldog

Charter Arms Police Bulldog

Charter Arms Police Bulldog
Caliber: 38 Special, 32 H&R Mag.
Action: Single and double action
Cylinder: 6-shot swing-out
Barrel: 2", 3½", 4"; tapered, bull, or shrouded barrel
Finish: Blue or stainless steel; checked walnut bulldog grips, square butt grips or Neoprene grips; add 25% for stainless steel; add 8% for shrouded barrel
Estimated Value: $160.00 - $200.00

Charter Arms Target Bulldog

Charter Arms Target Bulldog
Similar to the Bulldog except 4" barrel; shrouded ejector rod
Estimated Value: $140.00 - $175.00

Charter Arms Bulldog Pug

Charter Arms Bulldog Pug
Similar to the Bulldog except: 2½" shrouded barrel; add 20% for stainless steel model
Estimated Value: $170.00 - $215.00

Charter Arms Pathfinder

Charter Arms Pathfinder
Caliber: 22 long rifle, 22 magnum
Action: Single & double action
Cylinder: 6-shot, swing-out
Barrel: 2", 3", or 6" (3" & 6" only after 1987)
Finish: Blued or stainless steel; oil finished, plain or hand checkered walnut grips
Estimated Value: $160.00 - $200.00

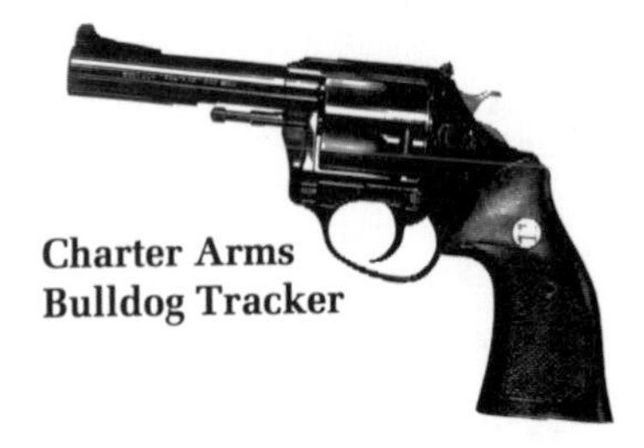
Charter Arms Bulldog Tracker

Charter Arms Bulldog Tracker
Caliber: 357 magnum and 38 special
Action: Single & double action
Cylinder: 5-shot, swing-out
Barrel: 2½", 4", or 6" bull barrel
Finish: Blued; checkered walnut square bull grips
Estimated Value: $175.00 - $215.00

Charter Arms Undercoverette & Lady Blue 32
Caliber: 32 S&W long
Action: Single & double action
Cylinder: 6-shot, swing-out
Barrel: 2"
Finish: Blued; oil finished, plain walnut grips
Estimated Value: $140.00 - $180.00

Charter Arms Undercover

Charter Arms Undercover
Caliber: 38 Special
Action: Single & double action
Cylinder: 5-shot, swing-out
Barrel: 2" or 3" (3" discontinued in 1990)
Finish: Blued, nickel, or stainless steel; oil finished, plain or hand checkered walnut grips or Neoprene grips; add 5% for nickel and 20% for S.S
Estimated Value: $145.00 - $185.00

Charter Arms Target Bulldog (Stainless Steel)

Charter Arms Police Bulldog 44 Special
Caliber: 44 Special
Action: Single or double, exposed hammer
Cylinder: 5-shot, swing-out
Barrel: 2½" or 3½" shrouded barrel with solid rib
Finish: Blued or stainless steel; bulldog checkered wood or neoprene grips. Add 12% for stainless steel
Estimated Value: $175.00 - $220.00

Charter Arms Target Bulldog (Stainless Steel)
Caliber: 357 magnum & 38 Special; 44 Special; 9mm
Action: Single or double, exposed hammer
Cylinder: 5-shot, swing-out, simultaneous ejector
Barrel: 5½" shrouded barrel with ventilated rib
Finish: Stainless steel with smooth wood target grips
Estimated Value: $255.00 - $315.00

Charter Arms Police Bulldog 357 Magnum
Caliber: 357 magnum & 38 Special
Action: Single or double, exposed hammer
Cylinder: 5-shot, swing-out, simultaneous ejector
Barrel: 4" shrouded barrel
Finish: Stainless steel; black neoprene grips
Estimated Value: $210.00 - $265.00

Charter Arms Pit Bull
Caliber: 9mm
Action: Single & double, exposed hammer, regular or bobbed
Cylinder: 5-shot, swing-out, simultaneous ejector
Barrel: 2½", 3½" shrouded barrel
Finish: Blued or stainless steel; neoprene grips. Add 8% for stainless steel
Estimated Value: $200.00 - $245.00

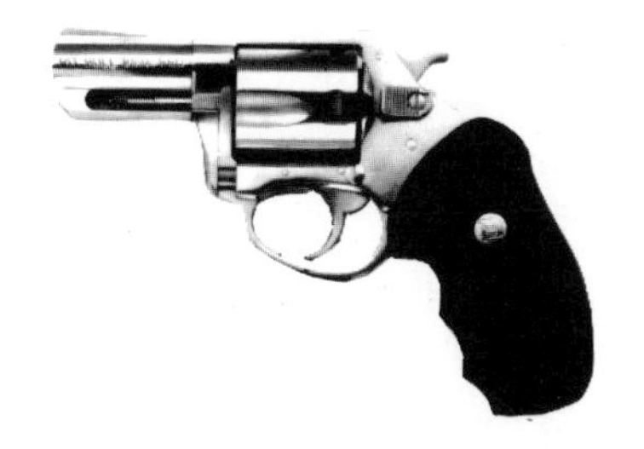

Charter Arms Pit Bull

Charter Arms Bonnie & Clyde Set
Caliber: 32 magnum (Bonnie); 38 Special (Clyde)
Action: Single & double action; exposed hammer
Cylinder: 6-shot, swing-out; fluted
Barrel: 2" shrouded barrel marked "Bonnie – 32 mag." or "Clyde – 38 spec."
Finish: Blued with smooth wood grips. These guns are sold as a set
Estimated Value: $365.00 - $460.00 *per set*

Charter Arms Pocket Target

Charter Arms Pocket Target
Caliber: 22 short, long, long rifle
Action: Single & double action; exposed hammer
Cylinder: 6-shot, swing-out
Barrel: 3"
Finish: Blued; plain grips or checkered walnut bulldog grips
Estimated Value: $120.00 - $150.00

Charter Arms Off Duty

Charter Arms Off Duty
Caliber: 38 Special; 22LR (after 1989)
Action: Single & double; exposed hammer
Cylinder: 5-shot, swing-out, fluted; 6-shot in 22 cal.
Barrel: 2" (shrouded barrel after 1989)
Finish: Flat black or stainless steel; smooth or checkered walnut or Neoprene grips; add 30% for S.S
Estimated Value: $125.00 - $160.00

Charter Arms Police Undercover
Caliber: 32 H&R magnum, 38 Special
Action: Single & double, pocket (bobbed) hammer available; exposed hammer
Cylinder: 6-shot, swing-out, fluted
Barrel: 2" or 4" (shrouded barrel only after 1989)
Finish: Blued or stainless steel; checkered walnut or Neoprene grips; add 12% for S.S
Estimated Value: $175.00 - $215.00

Charter Arms Police Undercover

Colt

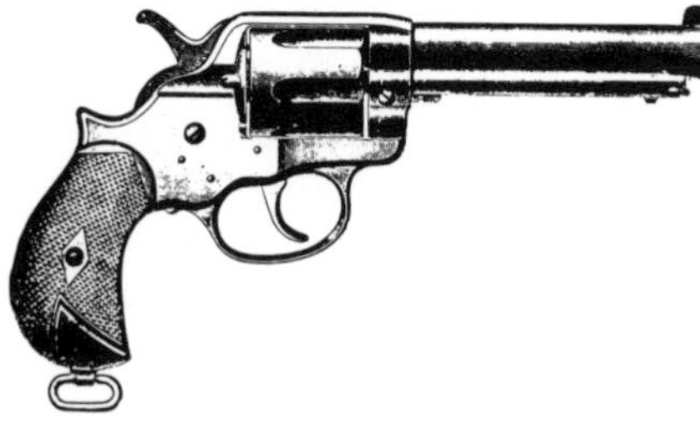

Colt Double Action Army Model

Colt Double Action Army Model
Caliber: 38-40, 44-40, 45 Colt
Action: Single or double action
Cylinder: 6-shot; ⅔ fluted; side load
Barrel: 3½" and 4" without side rod ejector; 4¾", 5½", and 7½" with the side rod ejector
Finish: Blued or nickel; hard rubber or checkered walnut grips; Lanyard loop in butt; also called "Double Action Frontier."
Estimated Value: $540.00 - $675.00

Colt Lightning Model
Caliber: 38 centerfire, 41 centerfire
Action: Single or double action
Cylinder: 6-shot; ⅔ fluted; side load; loading gate
Barrel: 2½", 3½", 4½", or 6"
Finish: Blued or nickel; hard rubber birds-head grips; no side rod ejector
Estimated Value: $480.00 - $600.00

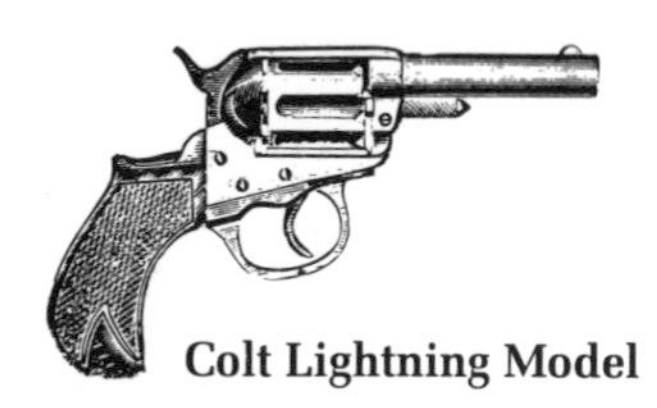

Colt Lightning Model

Colt Double Action Philippine Model
Same as Colt Double Action Army Model except larger trigger guard and trigger; originally made for the Army in Alaska but was sent to the Philippines instead
Estimated Value: $560.00 - $700.00

Colt New Army Model 1892

Colt New Army Model 1892
Caliber: 38 Colt short & long, 41 Colt short & long, 38 Special added in 1904, 32-30 added in 1905
Action: Single or double action
Cylinder: 6-shot; ⅔ fluted; swing out; simultaneous hand ejector
Barrel: 3", 4½", 6"
Finish: Blued or nickel; hard rubber or walnut grips; lanyard swivel attached to butt after 1900
Estimated Value: $400.00 - $500.00

Colt New Navy Model 1892
Similar to Colt New Army Model 1892 except has locking bolt and sometimes called New Army 2nd issue
Estimated Value: $440.00 - $550.00

Colt New Navy Model 1892

Colt New Pocket
Caliber: 32 short & long Colt
Action: Single or double action
Cylinder: 6-shot; swing out; simultaneous ejector
Barrel: 2½", 3½", or 6"
Finish: Blued or nickel; hard rubber grips
Estimated Value: $260.00 - $325.00

Colt Pocket Positive
Similar to the New Pocket with the positive locking system of the Police Positive; 32 short and long S&W cartridges or 32 Colt Police Positive
Estimated Value: $220.00 - $275.00

Colt New Police

Colt Army Model 1903
Same as Colt New Army Model 1892 except modified grip design; bore is slightly smaller in each caliber to increase accuracy
Estimated Value: $460.00 - $575.00

Colt New Pocket

Colt Pocket Positive

Colt New Police
Caliber: 32 Colt short & long, 32 Colt New Police (S&W long)
Action: Single or double action
Cylinder: 6-shot; swing out; simultaneous ejector
Barrel: 2½", 4", or 6"
Finish: Blued or nickel; hard rubber grips
Estimated Value: $240.00 - $300.00

Colt New Police Target
Same as Colt New Police except: 6" barrel only and blued finish; a target version of the New Police Model
Estimated Value: $270.00 - $350.00

Colt Bisley Model
Caliber: 32 long centerfire, 32-20 WCF, 38 long Colt CF, 38-40 WCF, 41 long Colt CF, 44 S&W Russian, 44-40 WCF, 45 Colt, 455 Eley
Action: Single action
Cylinder: 6-shot; half flute; side load
Barrel: 4¾", 5½", or 7½" with side rod ejector
Finish: Blued with case-hardened frame and hammer; checkered hard rubber grips
Estimated Value: $560.00 - $700.00

Colt Bisley Flat-Top Model
Similar to Colt Bisley Model except frame over the cylinder has a flat top; the longer barrel models were referred to as target models; wood, ivory, or hard rubber grips
Estimated Value: $800.00 - $1,000.00

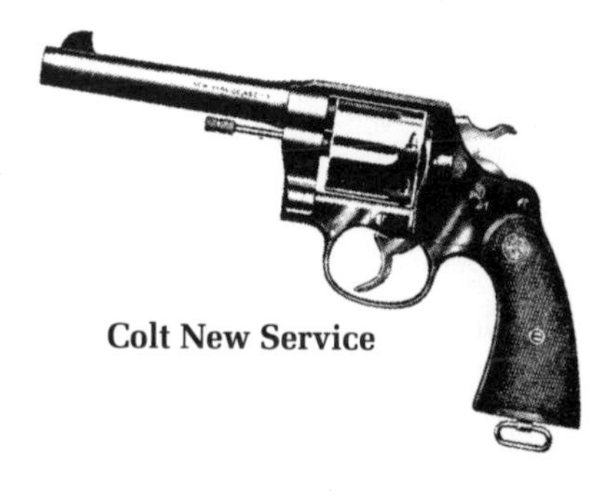

Colt New Service

Colt Police Positive

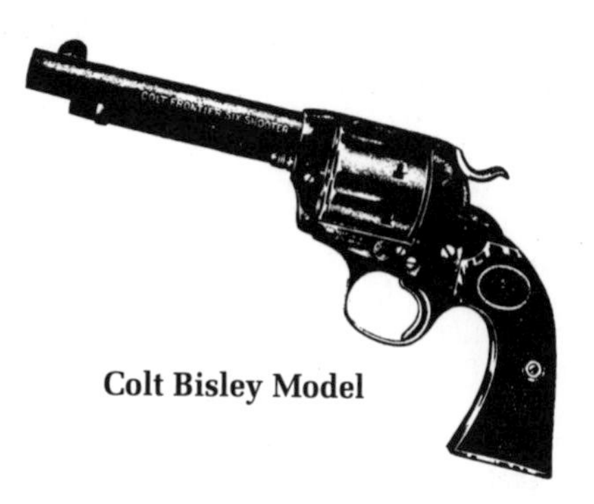

Colt Bisley Model

Colt New Service
Caliber: 38 special, 357 magnum (introduced about 1936), 38-40, 44-40, 44 Russian, 44 Special, 45 ACP, 45 Colt, 450 Eley, 455 Eley, and 476 Eley
Action: Single or double action
Cylinder: 6-shot; swing out; simultaneous ejector
Barrel: 4", 5", or 6" in 357 and 38 Special; 4½", 5½", or 7½" in other calibers; 4½" in 45 ACP (Model 1917 Revolver made for U.S. government during World War II)
Finish: Blued or nickel; checkered walnut grips
Estimated Value: $350.00 - $440.00

Colt Police Positive
Caliber: 32 short and long Colt (discontinued in 1915), 32 Colt New Police (32 S&W long), 38 New Police (38 S&W long)
Action: Single or double action
Cylinder: 6-shot; swing out; simultaneous ejector
Barrel: 2½", 4", 5", or 6"
Finish: Blued or nickel; hard rubber or checkered walnut grips; an improved version of the New Police with the Positive Lock feature which prevents the firing pin from contacting the cartridge until the trigger is pulled
Estimated Value: $220.00 - $275.00

Colt New Service Target
Caliber: Originally made for 44 Russian, 450 Eley, 455 Eley, and 476 Eley; later calibers were made for 44 Special, 45 Colt, and 45 ACP
Action: Single or double action
Cylinder: 6-shot; swing out; simultaneous ejector
Barrel: 6" and 7"
Finish: Blued; checkered walnut grips; hand-finished action
Estimated Value: $490.00 - $600.00

Colt New Service Target

Colt Police Positive Target

Colt Police Positive Target
Same as Colt Police Positive except 22 caliber long rifle regular from 1910 to 1932; 22 regular or hi-speed after 1932; 22 Winchester rim fire from 1910 to 1935; blued finish; 6" barrel only; checkered walnut grips
Estimated Value: $320.00 - $400.00

Colt Marine Corps Model 1905
Caliber: 38 Colt short and long
Action: Single or double action
Cylinder: 6-shot; ⅔ fluted; swing out; simultaneous hand ejector
Barrel: 6"
Finish: Blued or nickel; hard rubber or walnut grips
Estimated Value: $570.00 - $750.00

Colt Marine Corps Model 1905

Colt Police Positive Special
Caliber: 32-20 (discontinued in 1942), 32 New Police (S&W long), 38 Special
Action: Single or double action
Cylinder: 6-shot; swing out; simultaneous ejector
Barrel: 4", 5", 6"
Finish: Blued or nickel; checkered rubber, plastic, or walnut grips
Estimated Value: $200.00 - $250.00

Colt Police Positive Special

Colt Officers Model Target (1st Issue)
Caliber: 38 special
Action: Single or double action
Cylinder: 6-shot; ⅔ fluted; swing out; simultaneous ejector
Barrel: 6"
Finish: Blued; checkered walnut grips; hand-finished action
Estimated Value: $360.00 - $440.00

Colt Officers Model Target (1st Issue)

Colt Officers Model Target (2nd Issue)
Caliber: 22 long rifle (regular) 1930-32; 22 long rifle (Hi-speed) 1932-49; 32 Police Positive 1932-42; 38 Special 1908-49
Action: Single or double action
Cylinder: 6-shot; ⅔ fluted; swing out; simultaneous hand ejector
Barrel: 6" in 22 caliber & 32 Police Positive; 4", 4½", 5", 6", & 7½" in 38 Special
Finish: Blued; checkered walnut grips; hand-finished action, tapered barrel
Estimated Value: $285.00 - $375.00

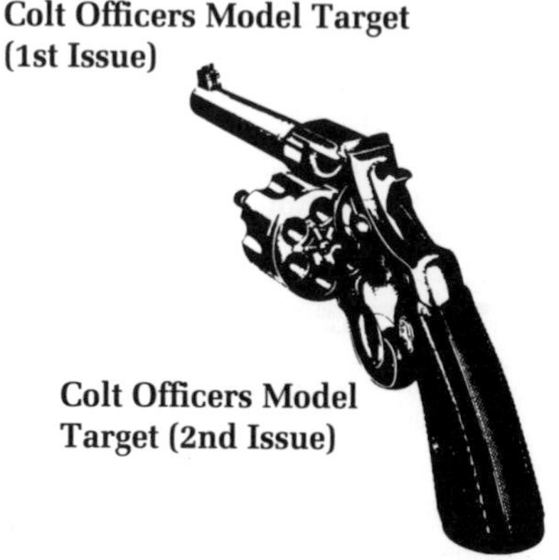

Colt Officers Model Target (2nd Issue)

Colt New Service Model 1909

Colt New Service Model 1909
Caliber: 32-20, 38 Special, 38-40, 42 Colt short & long, 44 Russian, 44-40, 45 Colt
Action: Single or double action
Cylinder: 6-shot; ⅔ fluted; swing out; simultaneous hand ejector
Barrel: 4", 4½", 5", 6"
Finish: Blued or nickel; hard rubber or walnut grips; also called "Army Special."
Estimated Value: $320.00 - $400.00

Colt Army Model 1917

Colt Army Model 1917
Caliber: 45 ACP or 45 ACP rim cartridges
Action: Single or double action
Cylinder: 6-shot; fluted; swing out; simultaneous hand ejector; used semi-circular clips to hold rimless case of 45 ACP
Barrel: 5½" round tapered
Finish: Blued; oiled-finished walnut grips
Estimated Value: $340.00 - $425.00

Colt Bankers Special
Caliber: 22 short, long, long rifle (Regular or Hi-Speed); 38 New Police (S&W long)
Action: Single or double action
Cylinder: 6-shot; swing out; simultaneous ejector
Barrel: 2"
Finish: Blued; checkered walnut grips; rounded grip after 1933
Estimated Value:
22 Cal.: $600.00 - $800.00
38 Cal.: $375.00 - $500.00

Colt Bankers Special

Colt Shooting Master

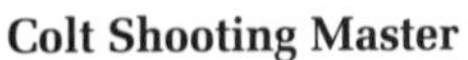

Colt Shooting Master
Caliber: 38 Special, 357 magnum (introduced in 1936), 44 Special, 45 ACP, 45 Colt
Action: Single or double action
Cylinder: 6-shot; swing out; simultaneous ejector
Barrel: 6"
Finish: Blued; checkered walnut grips
Estimated Value: $460.00 - $600.00

Colt Official Police (Model E-1)
Caliber: 22 long rifle (regular) introduced in 1930; 22 long rifle (Hi-Speed) introduced in 1932; 32-30 made from about 1928 to 1942; 38 Special made from 1928 to 1969; 41 long Colt made from 1928 to 1930
Action: Single or double action
Cylinder: 6-shot; fluted; swing out; simultaneous ejector
Barrel: 4" & 6" in 22 caliber; 4", 5", & 6" in 32-20; 2", 4", 5", & 6" in 41 caliber
Finish: Blued or nickel; checkered walnut or plastic grips; 41 caliber frame in all calibers
Estimated Value: $225.00 - $300.00

Colt Official Police

Colt Commando
Similar to Colt Official Police (Model E-1) except made to government specifications in 38 Special only; sandblasted blue finish
Estimated Value: $245.00 - $325.00

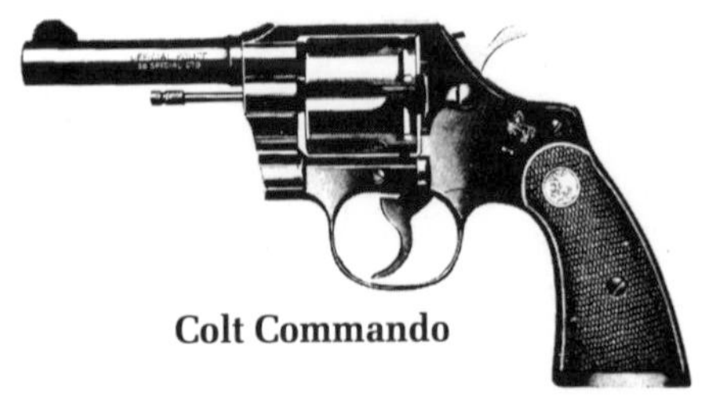
Colt Commando

Colt Detective Special
Caliber: 32 New Police (S&W long), 38 Special
Action: Single or double action
Cylinder: 6-shot; swing out; simultaneous ejector
Barrel: 2" & 3"
Finish: Blued or nickel; checkered walnut grips with rounded or square butt; with or without hammer shroud; add 10% for nickel finish
Estimated Value: $280.00 - $350.00

Colt Detective Special

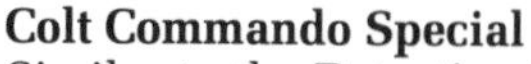

Colt Commando Special

Colt Commando Special
Similar to the Detective Special with matte finish & rubber grips
Estimated Value: $200.00 - $250.00

Colt Agent Light Weight

Colt Agent Light Weight
Similar to the Detective Special with matte finish; 2" barrel
Estimated Value: $175.00 - $220.00

Colt Cobra Model D-3
Caliber: 22 short & long rifle; 32 New Police (S&W long); 38 Special
Action: Single or double action
Cylinder: 6-shot, ⅔ fluted; swing out; simultaneous ejector
Barrel: 2", 3", 4", & 5"
Finish: Blued or nickel; checkered walnut grips; frame is made of a light alloy, but cylinder is steel; add $25.00 for nickel finish
Estimated Value: $200.00 - $250.00

Colt Cobra

Colt Officers Model Special
Caliber: 22 long rifle (regular & Hi-Speed); 38 Special
Action: Single or double action
Cylinder: 6-shot, ⅔ fluted; swing out; simultaneous ejector
Barrel: 6"
Finish: Blued; checkered plastic grips; replaced the Officers Model Target (2nd issue) with heavier non-tapered barrel & redesigned hammer.
Estimated Value: $225.00 - $300.00

Colt Officers Model Special

Colt Agent Model D-4

Colt Agent Model D-4
Caliber: 38 Special
Action: Single or double action
Cylinder: 6-shot, swing out; simultaneous ejector
Barrel: 2"
Finish: Blued; checkered walnut grips
Estimated Value: $170.00 - $225.00

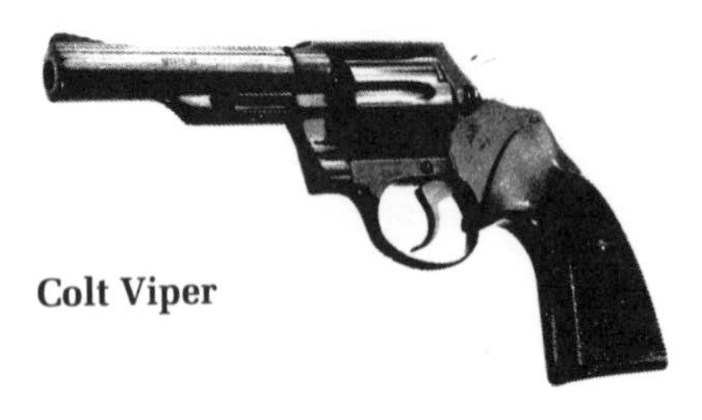
Colt Viper

Colt Air Crewman Special
Caliber: 38 Special
Action: Single or double action
Cylinder: 6-shot, swing out; simultaneous ejector; aluminum alloy
Barrel: 2"
Finish: Blued; checkered walnut grips;
Estimated Value: $680.00 - $850.00

Colt Officers Model Match

Colt Border Patrol
Caliber: 38 Special
Action: Single or double action
Cylinder: 6-shot, swing out; simultaneous ejector
Barrel: 4"
Finish: Blued; checkered walnut grips
Estimated Value: $600.00 - $800.00

Colt Viper
Caliber: 38 Special
Action: Single or double action
Cylinder: 6-shot, swing out
Barrel: 4"
Finish: Blued or nickel; checkered walnut wrap-around grips; alloy frame; add $20.00 for nickel
Estimated Value: $170.00 - $220.00

Colt Officers Model Match
Caliber: 22 long rifle, 38 Special
Action: Single or double action
Cylinder: 6-shot; swing out; simultaneous ejector; ⅔ fluted
Barrel: 6"
Finish: Blued; checkered walnut grips; heavy tapered barrel & wide hammer spur
Estimated Value: $240.00 - $320.00

Colt (.357) Three Fifty Seven

Colt (.357) Three Fifty Seven
Caliber: 357 magnum & 38 Special
Action: Single or double action
Cylinder: 6-shot; swing out; simultaneous ejector
Barrel: 4" & 6"
Finish: Blued; checkered walnut grips
Estimated Value: $225.00 - $280.00

Colt 38 Special Trooper
Caliber: 22, 38 Special
Action: Single or double action
Cylinder: 6-shot; swing out; simultaneous ejector
Barrel: 4" & 6"
Finish: Blued or nickel; checkered walnut square butt grips
Estimated Value: $210.00 - $275.00

Colt 38 Special Trooper

Colt Courier
Caliber: 22 short, long, long rifle, 32 New Police (S&W long)
Action: Single or double action
Cylinder: 6-shot; swing out; simultaneous ejector; made of lightweight alloy
Barrel: 3"
Finish: Dual tone blue; checkered plastic grips; frame & cylinder made of lightweight alloy; a limited production revolver
Estimated Value: $550.00 - $725.00

Colt Courier

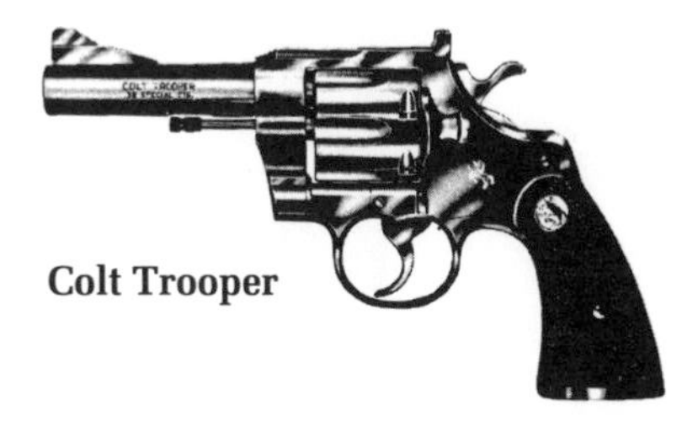

Colt Trooper

Colt Trooper
Caliber: 357 magnum & 38 Special
Action: Single or double action
Cylinder: 6-shot; swing out; simultaneous ejector
Barrel: 4" or 6"
Finish: Blued or nickel; checkered walnut, square butt grips
Estimated Value: $200.00 - $250.00

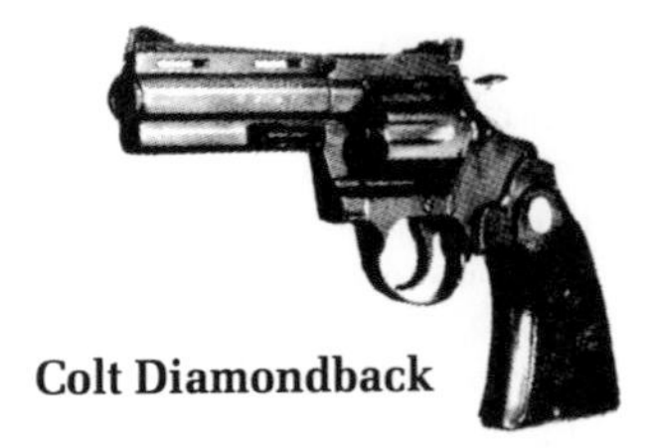

Colt Diamondback

Colt Diamondback
Caliber: 22, 22 long rifle, 38 Special
Action: Single or double
Cylinder: 6-shot; swing out; simultaneous ejector
Barrel: 2½", 4", or 6" ventilated rib
Finish: Blued or nickel; checkered walnut square butt grips; add 10% for nickel
Estimated Value: $300.00 - $375.00

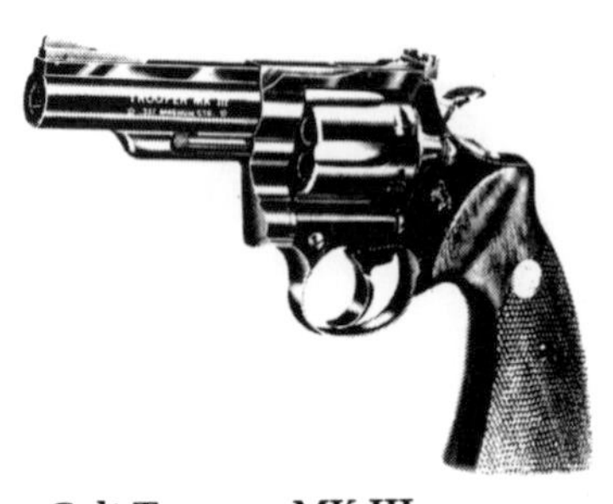

Colt Trooper MK III

Colt Trooper MK III
Caliber: 357 magnum & 38 Special; 22 long rifle & 22 WMR (added in 1979)
Action: Single or double action
Cylinder: 6-shot; swing out; simultaneous ejector
Barrel: 4", 6", or 8" (1980)
Finish: Blued or nickel; checkered walnut grips; wide target-type trigger & hammer; add $20.00 for nickel; $7.00 for 8" barrel
Estimated Value: $200.00 - $260.00

Colt Trooper MK V
Caliber: 357 magnum & 38 Special
Action: Single or double action; exposed hammer
Cylinder: 6-shot; swing out; simultaneous ejector
Barrel: 4" or 6" ventilated rib
Finish: Blued, nickel, or non-glare electroless plating (Colt-guard); checkered walnut grips; add 9% for nickel finish
Estimated Value: $205.00 - $270.00

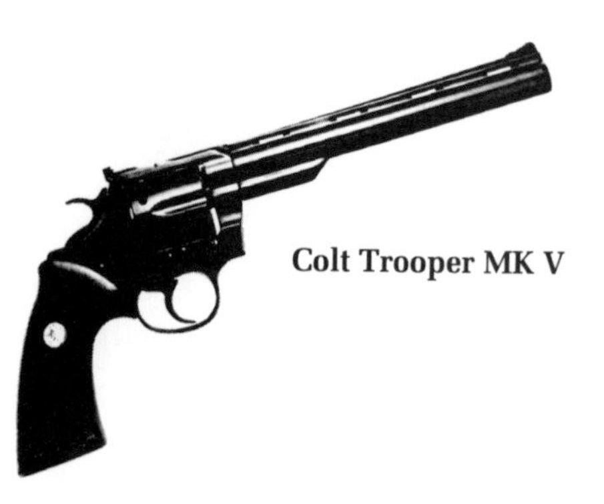

Colt Trooper MK V

Colt Lawman MK III
Caliber: 357 magnum & 38 Special
Action: Single or double action
Cylinder: 6-shot; swing out; simultaneous ejector
Barrel: 2" or 4"
Finish: Blued or nickel; checkered walnut grips; non-glare electroless plating; add $20.00 for nickel
Estimated Value: $175.00 - $230.00

Colt Lawman MK III

Colt Lawman MK V
Similar to the Trooper MKV with a 2" or 4" solid rib barrel, fixed sights; add $20.00 for nickel finish; discontinued in mid 1980's
Estimated Value: $190.00 - $250.00

Colt Lawman MK V

Colt King Cobra
Caliber: 357 magnum; 38 Special
Action: Single or double action
Cylinder: 6-shot; swing out; simultaneous ejector
Barrel: 2½", 4", 6", or 8"
Finish: Blued, matte stainless steel, or bright polished stainless steel; black rubber combat grips; solid barrel rib; add 6% for matte stainless steel; add 15% for polished stainless steel
Estimated Value: $245.00 - $305.00

Colt Model Python

Colt Official Police MK III

Colt Official Police MK III
Caliber: 38 Special
Action: Single or double
Cylinder: 6-shot; swing out; simultaneous ejector
Barrel: 4", 5", 6"
Finish: Blued; checkered walnut square butt grips
Estimated Value: $210.00 - $260.00

Colt Model I-3 Python, New Police Python, Python
Caliber: 357 mag., 38 Special; 22 long rifle & 22 WMR available in 1981 only
Action: Single or double action
Cylinder: 6-shot; swing out; simultaneous ejector
Barrel: 2½", 3", 4", 6", or 8" (after 1980); ventilated rib
Finish: Blued , nickel, non-glare electroless plating, or stainless steel; checkered walnut target grips; or rubber grips; add 17% for bright stainless steel; add 11% for satin stainless steel; add 4% for nickel
Estimated Value: $465.00 - $580.00

Colt Peacekeeper

Colt Peacekeeper
Caliber: 357 magnum & 38 Special
Action: Single or double action
Cylinder: 6-shot; swing out; simultaneous ejector
Barrel: 4" or 6" with ventilated rib & short ejector shroud
Finish: Non-glare matte blue combat finish with Colt rubber combat grips
Estimated Value: $190.00 - $250.00

Colt Single Action Army
Caliber: 357 magnum, 38 Special, 44 Special, 45 Colt
Action: Single action
Cylinder: 6-shot; side load with loading gate; under barrel ejector rod
Barrel: 4¾", 5½", or 7½"
Finish: Blued with case-hardened frame; composite rubber grips; nickel with checkered walnut grips; a revival of the Single Action Army Revolver, which was discontinued in 1941. The serial numbers start at 1001 SA; add $15.00 for a 7½" barrel; $60.00 for nickel
Estimated Value: $380.00 - $475.00

Colt Single Action Buntline Special
This is basically the same revolver as the Colt Single Action Army Revolver (1955 Model) except it is 45 Colt and 44 Special calibers only, with 12" barrel; add $90.00 for nickel finish
Estimated Value: $350.00 - $460.00

Colt New Frontier,
Single Action Army

Colt Anaconda
Caliber: 44 magnum, 44 Special
Action: Single or double action
Cylinder: 6-shot; swing out; simultaneous ejector
Barrel: 4", 6", or 8"; ventilated rib
Finish: Matte stainless steel; finger-grooved rubber combat grips
Estimated Value: $325.00 - $405.00

Colt Single Action Army

Colt New Frontier,
Single Action Army
This is the same handgun as the Colt Single Action Army revolver except frame is flat topped; finish is high polished; adjustable rear sight (wind & elevation); blued case-hardened finish with smooth walnut grips. This is a target version of the SA Army; made in 44-40, 44 Spec., & 45 Colt calibers; add $20.00 for 7½" barrel
Estimated Value: $375.00 - $500.00

Colt Frontier Scout
Caliber: 22 & 22 WRF (interchangeable cylinder)
Action: Single action
Cylinder: 6-shot side load; loading gate; under barrel ejector rod
Barrel: 4¾" or 9½" (Buntline Scout)
Finish: Blued or nickel; plastic or wood grips; single Action Army replica ¾ scale size in 22 caliber; with bright alloy frame or blued steel frame; add $10.00 for interchangeable cylinder, $10.00 for nickel finish, $10.00 for Buntline Scout
Estimated Value: $190.00 - $240.00

Colt Frontier Scout

Colt Peacemaker 22 Single Action

Colt Peacemaker 22 Single Action
Caliber: 22, 22 WRF (when equipped with dual cylinder)
Action: Single
Cylinder: 6-shot side load; loading gate; under barrel ejector rod
Barrel: 4¾", 6", & 7½"
Finish: Blued barrel & cylinder; case-hardened frame; black composite rubber grips; all steel; 22 caliber version of the 45 Peacemaker; add $6.00 for 7½" barrel; add $10.00 for extra cylinder
Estimated Value: $175.00 - $220.00

Colt New Frontier
Same as the Colt Peacemaker 22 SA except adjustable rear sight; flat top frame
Estimated Value: $200.00 - $250.00

Colt New Frontier

Colt New Frontier Buntline Special
This revolver is the same as the Colt New Frontier (1961 Model) except 45 caliber ; 12" barrel.
Estimated Value: $395.00 - $525.00

Dan Wesson

Dan Wesson Model 11

Dan Wesson Model 11
Caliber: 357 magnum or 38 Special (interchangeable)
Action: Double or single; exposed hammer; simultaneous ejector
Cylinder: 6-shot; swing out
Barrel: 2½", 4", 6"; interchangeable barrels
Finish: Blued; one-piece changeable walnut grip; barrels and shroud can be changed by means of a recessed barrel nut
Estimated Value: $160.00 - $200.00

Dan Wesson Model 12
Same as Model 11 except target model with adjustable rear sight
Estimated Value: $170.00 - $215.00

Dan Wesson Model 14, 14-2, 714
Caliber: 357 magnum or 38 Special (interchangeable)
Action: Double or single; exposed hammer; simultaneous ejector
Cylinder: 6-shot; swing out;
Barrel: 2½", 4", or 6"; interchangeable barrels
Finish: Blued, satin blue, or 714 stainless steel; one-piece walnut grip; add $15.00 for bright blue finish; add $40.00 for stainless steel
Estimated Value: $150.00 - $210.00

Dan Wesson Model 14

Dan Wesson Model 15
Similar to the Model 14 except adjustable rear sight
Estimated Value: $160.00 - $220.00

Dan Wesson Model 8-2, 708
Similar to Model 14 except 38 caliber only; add $15.00 for bright blue finish; add $40.00 for stainless steel (708)
Estimated Value: $150.00 - $200.00

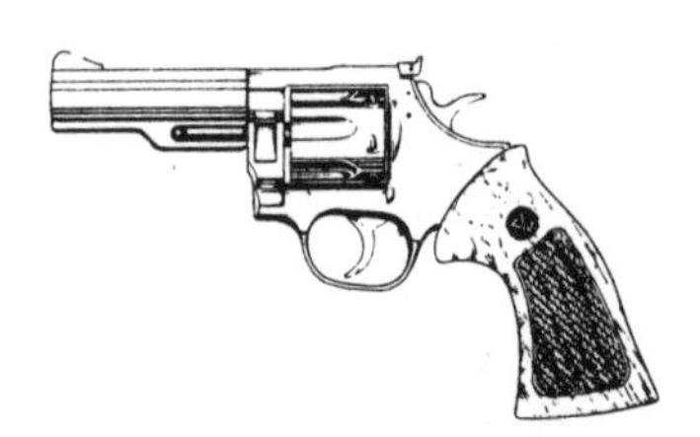

Dan Wesson Model 8-2

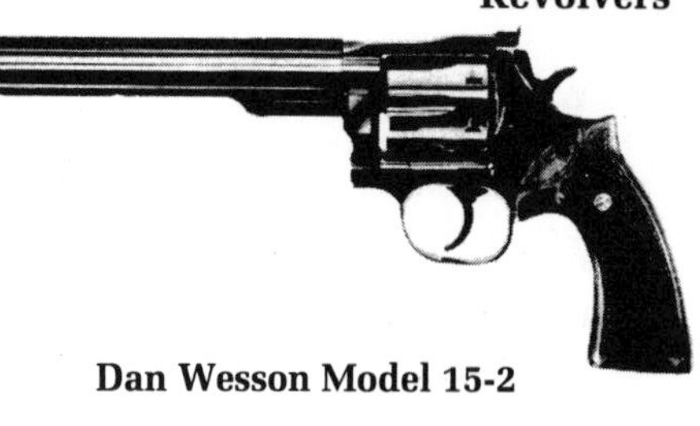

Dan Wesson Model 15-2

Dan Wesson Model 15-2, 715
Caliber: 357 magnum or 38 Special (interchangeable)
Action: Double or single; exposed hammer
Cylinder: 6-shot; swing out; simultaneous ejector
Barrel: 2½", 4", 6", 8", 10", 12", or 15" interchangeable barrels
Finish: Blued or stainless steel; checkered wood target grips; add $25.00 for stainless steel (715)
Estimated Value: $200.00 - $290.00

Dan Wesson Model 9-2

Dan Wesson Model 15-2H

Dan Wesson Model 15-2H
Same as Model 15-2 except it has a heavier bull barrels
Estimated Value: $210.00 - $300.00

Dan Wesson Model 15-2V, 715-V
Same as Model 15-2 except it has ventilated rib; add $25.00 for stainless steel (715-V)
Estimated Value: $215.00 - $315.00

Dan Wesson Model 15-2VH, 715-VH
Same as Model 15-2 except it has a heavier bull barrel with ventilated rib assembly; add $25.00 for stainless steel (715-VH)
Estimated Value: $230.00 - $350.00

Dan Wesson Model 9-2, 709
Similar to Model 15-2 except 38 caliber only; no 12" or 15" barrel; add $25.00 for stainless steel (709)
Estimated Value: $190.00 - $280.00

Dan Wesson Model 9-2V, 709-V
Similar to Model 9-2 with ventilated rib; add $25.00 for stainless steel (709-V)
Estimated Value: $210.00 - $310.00

Dan Wesson Model 9-2VH, 709-VH
Similar to Model 9-2 with heavier bull barrel & ventilated rib; add $25.00 for stainless steel (709-VH)
Estimated Value: $225.00 - $340.00

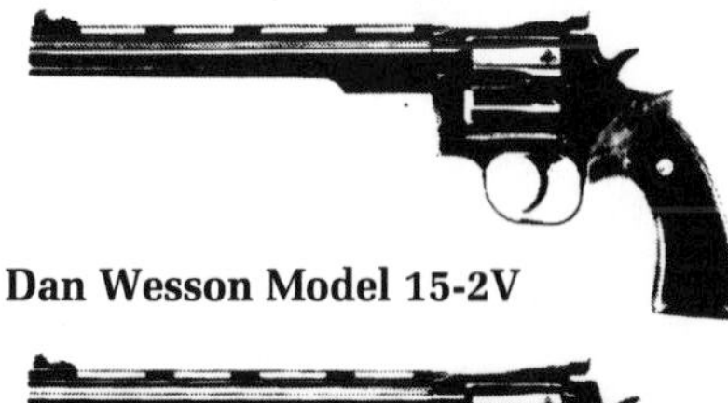

Dan Wesson Model 15-2V

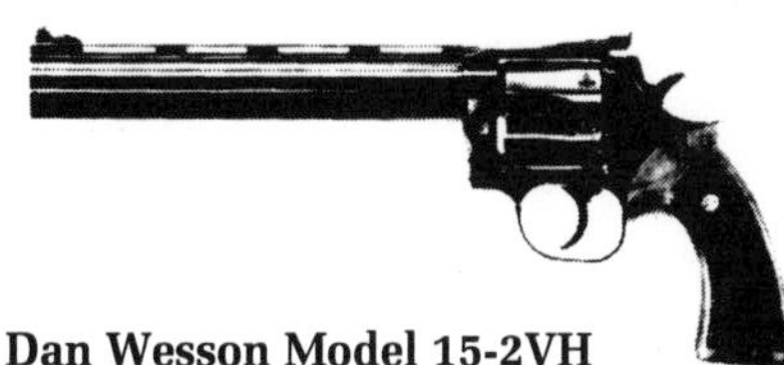

Dan Wesson Model 15-2VH

Dan Wesson Model 22, 722
Similar to the Model 15-2 in 22 caliber only; not available with 10", 12", or 15" barrel; add $25.00 for stainless steel (722).
Estimated Value: $200.00 - $275.00

Dan Wesson Model 22V

Dan Wesson Model 22M, 722M
Similar to the Model 22 in 22 magnum caliber; add $30.00 for stainless steel (722M)
Estimated Value: $210.00 - $285.00

Dan Wesson Model 22M-V, 722M-V
Similar to the Model 22-V in 22 magnum caliber; add $30.00 for stainless steel finish (722M-V)
Estimated Value: $220.00 - $305.00

Dan Wesson Model 22M-VH, 722M-VH
Similar to the Model 22-VH except 22 magnum caliber; add $30.00 for stainless steel (722M-VH)
Estimated Value: $240.00 - $320.00

Dan Wesson Model 32

Dan Wesson Model 22V, 722-V
Similar to the Model 22 except ventilated rib; add $30.00 for stainless steel (722-V)
Estimated Value: $215.00 - $300.00

Dan Wesson Model 22-VH, 722-VH
Similar to the Model 22 except heavier bull barrier & ventilated rib; add $30.00 for stainless steel (722-VH)
Estimated Value: $230.00 - $310.00

Dan Wesson Model 32, 732
Similar to the Model 15-2 in 32 magnum caliber; 2½", 4", 6", or 8" barrel; add $30.00 for stainless steel (732)
Estimated Value: $200.00 - $275.00

Dan Wesson Model 32-V, 732-V
Similar to the Model 32 except ventilated rib; add $30.00 for stainless steel (732-V)
Estimated Value: $215.00 - $300.00

Dan Wesson Model 32-VH, 732-VH
Similar to the Model 32 except ventilated rib; heavy barrel; add $30.00 for stainless steel (732-VH)
Estimated Value: $230.00 - $310.00

Dan Wesson Model 40-V 357 Super Mag, 740-V
Caliber: 357 Maximum
Action: Double & single; exposed hammer; simultaneous ejector
Cylinder: 6-shot; swing out; fluted
Barrel: 4", 6", 8", or 10" interchangeable barrels; ventilated rib
Finish: Blued or stainless steel (740-V); smooth walnut grips; each model comes with an extra barrel; add $60.00 for stainless steel
Estimated Value: $295.00 - $410.00

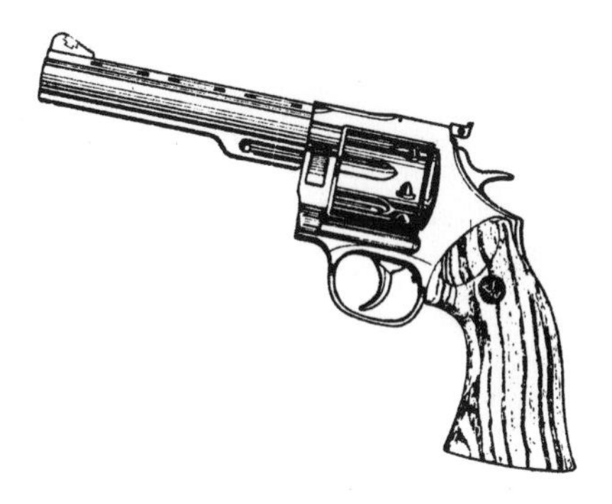

Dan Wesson Model 40-V

Dan Wesson Model 40-V8S, 740-V8S
Similar to the Model 40-V with slotted barrel shroud; 8" barrel only; add $60.00 for stainless steel (740-V8S)
Estimated Value: $310.00 - $420.00

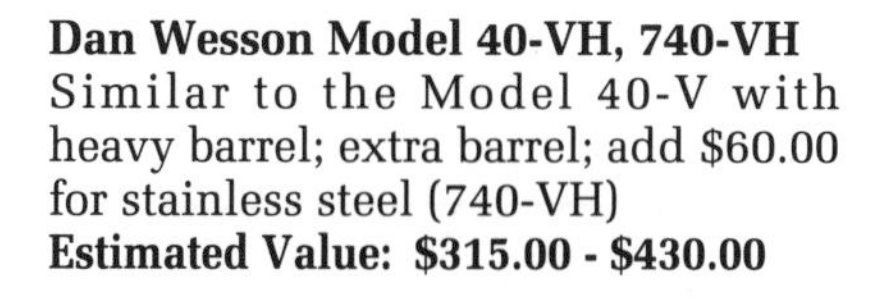

Dan Wesson Model 40-VH, 740-VH
Similar to the Model 40-V with heavy barrel; extra barrel; add $60.00 for stainless steel (740-VH)
Estimated Value: $315.00 - $430.00

Dan Wesson Model 375V Super Mag
Similar to the Model 40V except 375 magnum caliber
Estimated Value: $300.00 - $410.00

Dan Wesson Model 375V Super Mag

Dan Wesson Model 375-V8S Super Mag
Similar to the Model 375 V except slotted barrel shroud; 8" barrel
Estimated Value: $320.00 - $400.00

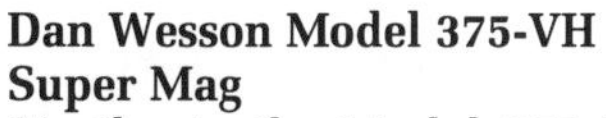

Dan Wesson Model 375-VH Super Mag
Similar to the Model 375 V except heavy barrel
Estimated Value: $305.00 - $430.00

Dan Wesson Model 44V

Dan Wesson Model 44-V, 744-V
Caliber: 44 magnum, 44 Special (jacketed only)
Action: Single & double, exposed hammer, wide hammer, & trigger
Cylinder: 6-shot; swing out; simultaneous ejector
Barrel: 4", 6", 8", or 10" interchangeable barrel; ventilated rib
Finish: Blued or stainless steel (744-V); smooth or checkered walnut grips with thumb flute; add $70.00 for stainless steel (744-V)
Estimated Value: $255.00 - $350.00

Dan Wesson Model 45-V Colt, 745-V
Caliber: 45 Colt
Action: Single & double, exposed hammer, wide hammer, & trigger
Cylinder: 6-shot; swing out; simultaneous ejector
Barrel: 4", 6", 8", or 10" ventilated rib
Finish: Blued or stainless steel (745-V); smooth walnut grips; add $70.00 for stainless steel (745-V)
Estimated Value: $260.00 - $350.00

Dan Wesson Model 45-VH, 745-VH
Similar to the Model 45-V except heavier bull barrel; add $70.00 for stainless steel (745-VH)
Estimated Value: $270.00 - $370.00

Dan Wesson Model 44-VH, 744-VH
Similar to the Model 44 except heavier bull barrel; add $70.00 for stainless steel (744-VH)
Estimated Value: $270.00 - $370.00

Dan Wesson Model 41V, 741-V
Similar to the Model 44V except 41 magnum caliber; add $50.00 for stainless steel finish (741-V)
Estimated Value: $250.00 - $335.00

Dan Wesson Model 41-VH, 741-VH
Similar to the Model 44VH except 41 magnum caliber; add $50.00 for stainless steel finish (741-VH)
Estimated Value: 260.00 - $360.00

Great Western

Great Western Frontier

Great Western Frontier
Caliber: 22 short, long, long rifle, 357 magnum, 38 Special, 44 magnum, 44 Special, 45 Colt
Action: Single, hand ejector rod
Cylinder: 6-shot clip
Barrel: 4¾", 5½", or 7½" round barrel with ejector housing under barrel
Finish: Blued; imitation stag grip; a replica of the Colt Single Action revolver; Values of these revolvers vary due to the poor quality of the early models; they were also available in unassembled kit form.
Estimated Value: $175.00 - $300.00

Harrington & Richardson

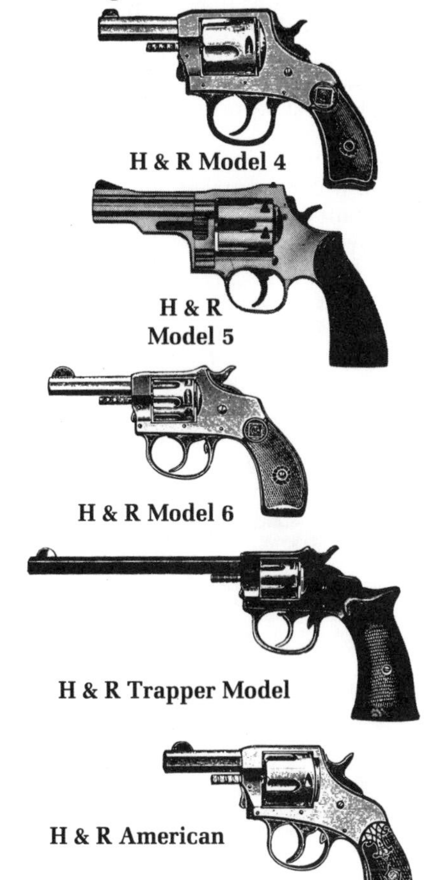

H & R Model 4

H & R Model 5

H & R Model 6

H & R Trapper Model

H & R American

H & R Model 4
Caliber: 32 S&W, 32 S&W long, 38 S&W
Action: Double & single; exposed hammer; solid frame; side load
Cylinder: 6-shot in 32 caliber, 5-shot in 38 caliber
Barrel: 2½", 4½", or 6" hexagon barrel
Finish: Blued or nickel; hard rubber grips
Estimated Value: $75.00 - $100.00

H & R Model 5
Similar to the Model 4 except: 32 S&W caliber only; smaller frame and cylinder (5 shot)
Estimated Value: $70.00 - $90.00

H & R Model 6
Similar to the Model 5 except: 22 short, long, long rifle; 7-shot cylinder; minor change in shape of top of frame at rear of cylinder
Estimated Value: $75.00 - $100.00

H & R Trapper Model
Same as Model 6 except 6" barrel, checkered square butt walnut grips
Estimated Value: $ 95.00 - $120.00

H & R Hunter Model (1926)
Same as Trapper Model except 10" barrel
Estimated Value: $85.00 - $110.00

H & R Hunter Model (1930)
Similar to Hunter Model (1926) except: larger frame; 9-shot safety cylinder (recessed chambers)
Estimated Value: $ 90.00 - $115.00

H & R American
Caliber: S&W, 32 S&W long; 38 S&W
Action: Single or double; exposed hammer; solid frame; side load
Cylinder: 6-shot in 32 caliber; 5-shot in 38 caliber
Barrel: 2½", 4½", or 6" hexagon barrel
Finish: Blued or nickel; hard rubber round butt grips
Estimated Value: $80.00 - $100.00

H & R Young American
Caliber: 22 short, long, long rifle, 32 S&W short
Action: Single or double; exposed hammer; solid frame; side load
Cylinder: 7-shot in 22 caliber; 5-shot in 32 caliber
Barrel: 2", 4½", or 6" hexagon barrel
Finish: Blued or nickel; hard rubber round butt grips
Estimated Value: $75.00 - $100.00

H & R Young American

H & R Vest Pocket
Same as H & R Young American except 1⅛" barrel only; double action only; no spur on hammer
Estimated Value: $70.00 - $90.00

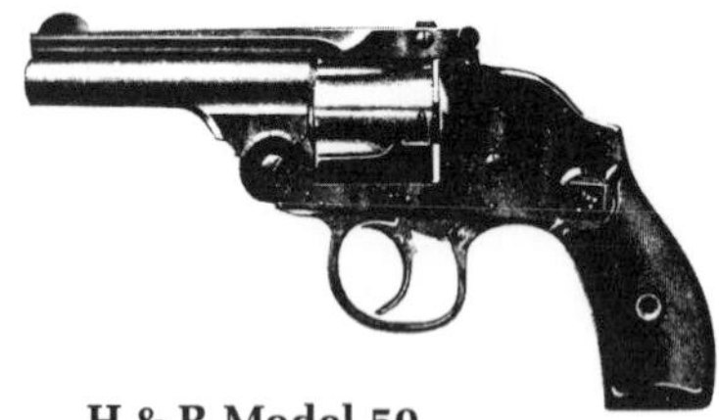
H & R Model 50

H & R Premier

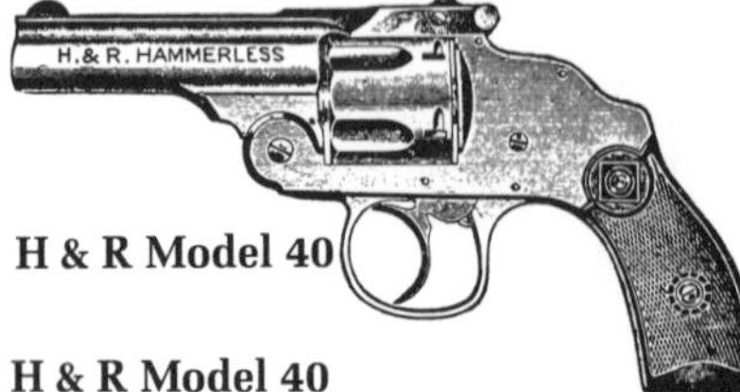

H & R Model 40

H & R Model 40
Same as Premier except double action only; concealed hammer; frame completely encloses hammer
Estimated Value: $100.00 - $135.00

H & R Automatic Ejecting Revolver
Caliber: 32 S&W, 32 S&W long; 38 S&W
Action: Single or double; exposed hammer; hinged frame; top break
Cylinder: 6-shot in 32 caliber; 5-shot in 38 caliber; simultaneous automatic ejector
Barrel: 3¼", 4", 5", or 6" round barrel with rib
Finish: Blued or nickel; hard rubber round butt grips
Estimated Value: $95.00 - $120.00

H & R Model 50
Same as Automatic Ejecting Revolver except: double action only; concealed hammer; frame completely encloses hammer area
Estimated Value: $100.00 - $125.00

H & R Premier
Caliber: 22 short, long, long rifle, 32 S&W
Action: Single or double; exposed hammer; small hinged frame; top break
Cylinder: 7-shot in 22 caliber; 5-shot in 32 caliber; simultaneous automatic ejector
Barrel: 2", 3", 4", 5", or 6" round ribbed barrel
Finish: Blued or nickel; hard rubber round butt grips
Estimated Value: $105.00 - $130.00

H & R Model 944

H & R Model 945

H & R Model 922
Caliber: 22 short, long, long rifle
Action: Single or double; exposed hammer; solid frame; side load
Cylinder: 9-shot removable cylinder
Barrel: 4", 6", or 10" octagon barrel in early models, later models had 2½", 4", or 6" round barrel
Finish: Blued; checkered walnut grips on early models; plastic grips on later models
Estimated Value: $80.00 - $100.00

H & R Model 923
Same as Model 922 except nickel finish
Estimated Value: $85.00 - $105.00

H & R Model 944
Caliber: 22 short, long, long rifle, 22 WRF
Action: Single or double; exposed hammer; heavy hinged frame; top break
Cylinder: 9-shot; simultaneous automatic ejector
Barrel: 6" round ribbed barrel
Finish: Blued; checkered square butt walnut grips
Estimated Value: $105.00 - $130.00

H & R Model 945
Same as Model 944 except safety cylinder (recessed chambers)
Estimated Value: $110.00 - $135.00

H & R Model 955
Same as Model 945 except: 10" barrel
Estimated Value: $115.00 - $130.00

H & R Model 922

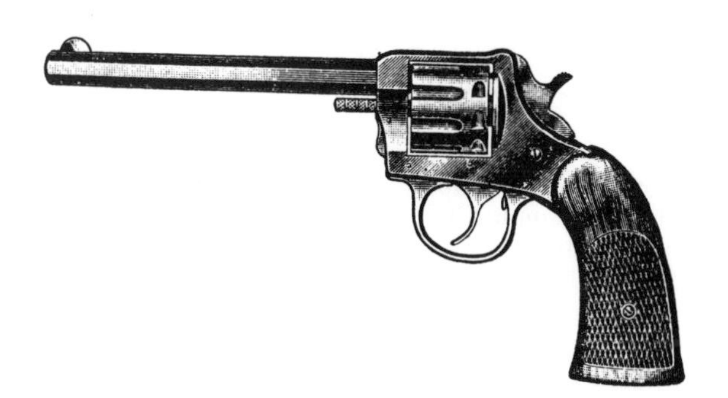

H & R Model 766 Target

H & R No. 199 Sportsman

H & R No. 199 (Sportsman)
Caliber: 22 short, long, long rifle
Action: Single or double; exposed hammer; hinged frame; top break
Cylinder: 9-shot; simultaneous automatic ejector
Barrel: 6" round ribbed barrel
Finish: Blued; checkered square butt walnut grips
Estimated Value: $100.00 - $125.00

H & R Defender 38
Similar to No. 199 Sportsman Model except: 38 S&W caliber; 4" or 6" barrel; plastic grips
Estimated Value: 110.00 - $140.0

H & R Model 299 New Defender
Similar to No. 199 Sportsman Model except 2" barrel
Estimated Value: $105.00 - $135.00

H & R No. 999 (Deluxe Sportsman)
Same as No. 199 Sportsman Model except redesigned hammer & barrel rib in 1950's; 32 caliber (6-shot cylinder) & 4" barrel available in 1979.
Estimated Value: $120.00 - $160.00

H & R 766 Target
Caliber: 22 short, long, long rifle, 22WRF
Action: Single or double; exposed hammer; small hinged frame; top break
Cylinder: 7-shot; simultaneous automatic ejector
Barrel: 6" round ribbed barrel
Finish: Blued; checkered square butt walnut grips
Estimated Value: $100.00 - $135.00

H & R Ultra Sportsman
Caliber: 22 short, long, long rifle, 22 WRF
Action: Single or double; exposed hammer; top break; wide hammer spur
Cylinder: 9-shot; simultaneous automatic ejector
Barrel: 6" round ribbed barrel
Finish: Blued; checkered square butt walnut grips
Estimated Value: $120.00 - $145.00

H & R Model 999 Deluxe Sportsman

H & R Model 299 New Defender

H & R Bobby Model 15
Caliber: 32 S&W, 32 S&W long, 38 S&W
Action: Single or double; exposed hammer; hinged frame; top break
Cylinder: 6-shot in 32 caliber, 5-shot in 38 caliber; simultaneous automatic ejector
Barrel: 4" round, ribbed
Finish: Blued; checkered square butt walnut grips
Estimated Value: $ 95.00 - $120.00

H & R Model 929 Side-Kick

H & R Model 632

H & R Model 929 & 930 Side-Kick
Caliber: 22 short, long, long rifle
Action: Single or double; exposed hammer; solid frame
Cylinder: 9-shot swing out; simultaneous manual ejector
Barrel: 2½", 4", or 6" round ribbed
Finish: Blued or nickel; checkered plastic grips; 930 is nickel finish
Estimated Value: $ 80.00 - $100.00

H & R Model 732 Guardsman

H & R Model 622 & 623
Caliber: 22 short, long, long rifle
Action: Single or double; exposed hammer; solid frame; side load
Cylinder: 6-shot removable
Barrel: 2½", 4", or 6" round
Finish: Blued or nickel; 623 is nickel finish; checkered plastic grips
Estimated Value: $65.00 - $80.00

H & R Model 642
Similar to the Model 622 in 22 WMR caliber; 2½" or 4" barrel
Estimated Value: $75.00 - $90.00

H & R Model 632 & 633
Caliber: 32 S&W, 32 S&W long
Action: Single or double; exposed hammer; solid frame
Cylinder: 6-shot
Barrel: 2½" or 4" round
Finish: Blued or nickel; 633 is nickel finish; checkered tenite round or square butt grips
Estimated Value: $70.00 - $90.00

H & R Model 732 & 733 Guardsman
Caliber: 32 S&W, 32 S&W long
Action: Single or double; exposed hammer; solid frame
Cylinder: 6-shot swing out; simultaneous manual ejector
Barrel: 2½" or 4" round
Finish: Blued or nickel; 733 is nickel finish; checkered plastic grips; walnut grips available after 1982; add $10.00 for walnut
Estimated Value: $ 80.00 - $105.00

H & R Model 622

H & R Model 939 Ultra Sidekick

H & R Model 939 & 940 Ultra Sidekick
Caliber: 22 short, long, long rifle
Action: Single or double; exposed hammer; solid frame
Cylinder: 9-shot swing out; simultaneous manual ejector
Barrel: 6" ventilated rib target barrel; 940 has bull barrel
Finish: Blued; checkered walnut grips with thumb rest
Estimated Value: $ 90.00 - $110.00

H & R Model 903
Similar to the Model 939 with a solid heavy flat side barrel
Estimated Value: $ 95.00 - $120.00

H & R Model 603
Similar to the Model 903 in 22 magnum
Estimated Value: $ 95.00 - $120.00

H & R Model 904 & 905
Similar to the Model 903 with a 4" or 6" heavy round barrel. Blue satin finish available after 1982. Model 905 has nickel finish.
Estimated Value: $100.00 - $130.00

H & R Model 604
Similar to the Model 904 except 22 magnum
Estimated Value: $105.00 - $135.00

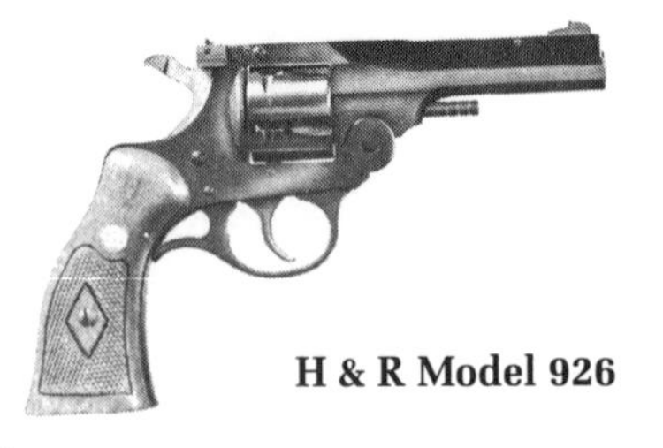
H & R Model 926

H & R Model 900

H & R Model 900 & 901
Caliber: 22 short, long, long rifle
Action: Single or double; exposed hammer; solid frame; side load
Cylinder: 9-shot removable
Barrel: 2½", 4", or 6"
Finish: Blued or nickel; 901 is nickel; checkered plastic grips
Estimated Value: $75.00 - $95.00

H & R Model 925 Defender
Caliber: 38 S&W
Action: Single or double; exposed hammer; hinged frame; top break
Cylinder: 5-shot; simultaneous automatic ejector
Barrel: 2½" round, ribbed
Finish: Blued; one-piece wrap-around grip
Estimated Value: $ 95.00 - $120.00

H & R Model 926
Caliber: 38 S&W
Action: Single or double; exposed hammer; hinged frame; top break
Cylinder: 5-shot; simultaneous automatic ejector
Barrel: 4"
Finish: Blued; checkered plastic square butt grips
Estimated Value: $100.00 - $125.00

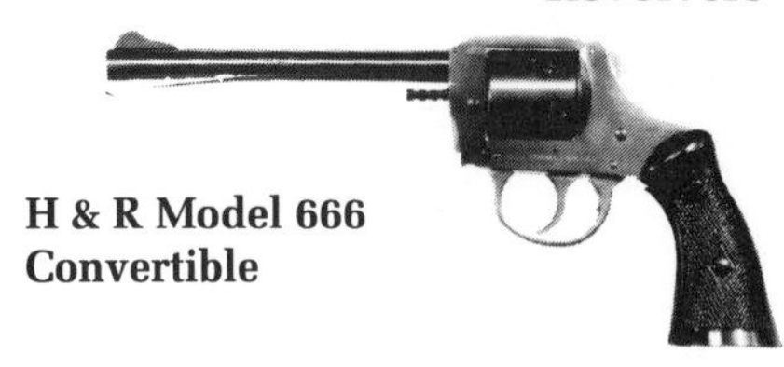

H & R Model 666 Convertible

H & R Model 666 Convertible
Caliber: 22 short, long, long rifle, 22 magnum (WMR) with extra interchangeable cylinder
Action: Single or double; exposed hammer; solid frame; side load
Cylinder: 6-shot removable; extra interchangeable cylinder so either cartridge can be used
Barrel: 6" round
Finish: Blued; black cycolac, square butt grips
Estimated Value: $75.00 - $105.00

H & R Model 949

H & R Model 949 & 950 Forty-Niner
Caliber: 22 short, long, long rifle
Action: Single or double; exposed hammer; solid frame; side load & ejection
Cylinder: 9-shot
Barrel: 5½" round; ejector rod under barrel
Finish: Blued or nickel; 950 is nickel; smooth walnut, one-piece, western style grips
Estimated Value: $70.00 - $95.00

H & R Model 976
Similar to 949 except 7½" barrel; case-hardened frame; add $20.00 for nickel finish
Estimated Value: $ 80.00 - $100.00

H & R Model 649 Convertible

H & R Model 649 & 650 Convertible
Caliber: 22 short, long, long rifle, 22 magnum (WMR) with extra interchangeable cylinder
Action: Single or double; exposed hammer; solid frame; side load & ejection
Cylinder: 6-shot removable cylinder; single manual ejector; extra interchangeable cylinder
Barrel: 5½" or 7½" round barrel; ejector rod housing under barrel
Finish: Blued barrel; satin finish frame or nickel finish; smooth western-style walnut grips; 650 is nickel finish
Estimated Value: $ 85.00 - $115.00

H & R Model 676 Convertible
Similar to Model 649 Convertible except 4½", 5½", 7½", or 12" barrel; blued barrel with antique color case hardened frame; finger rest at rear of trigger guard; add $25.00 for 12" barrel
Estimated Value: $ 95.00 - $120.00

H & R Model 686 Convertible
Similar to the Model 676 except ramp front sight, adjustable rear sight; add $25.00 for 12" barrel
Estimated Value: $100.00 - $135.00

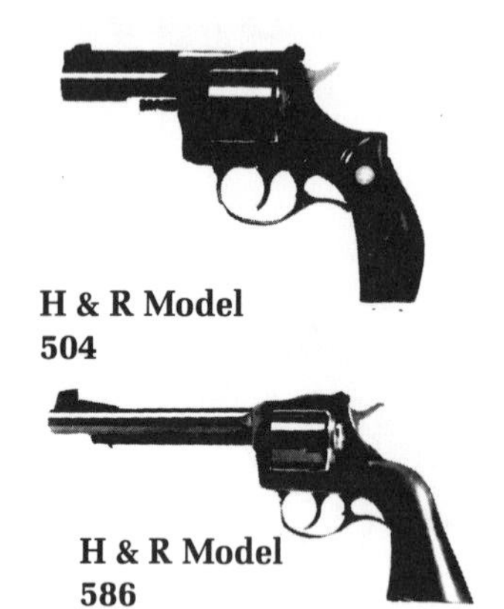

H & R Model 504

H & R Model 586

H & R Model 504
Caliber: 32 H&R magnum
Action: Single or double; swing-out cylinder; exposed hammer
Cylinder: 5-shot swing out
Barrel: 3", 4", 6" target bull
Finish: Blued; smooth walnut grips, round or square butt
Estimated Value: $120.00 - $150.00

H & R Model 586
Caliber: 32 H&R magnum
Action: Single or double; side loading & ejection
Cylinder: 5-shot removable
Barrel: 4½", 5½", 7½", or 10" round
Finish: Blued; case-hardened frame; hardwood grips
Estimated Value: $110.00 - $145.00

H & R Model 829 & 830
Caliber: 22 long rifle
Action: Single or double; exposed hammer
Cylinder: 9-shot swing out
Barrel: 3" bull barrel
Finish: Blued or nickel; 830 is nickel finish; smooth walnut grips
Estimated Value: $ 95.00 - $125.00

H & R Model 829

H & R Model 826
Similar to the Model 829 in 22 magnum caliber
Estimated Value: $100.00 - $125.00

H & R Model 832 & 833
Similar to the Model 829 in 32 caliber; Model 833 has nickel finish
Estimated Value: $100.00 - $125.00

H & R Model 532
Caliber: 32 H&R magnum
Action: Single or double; side load
Cylinder: 5-shot removable
Barrel: 2¼", 4" round
Finish: Blued; smooth walnut grips
Estimated Value: $ 80.00 - $100.00

H & R Model 532

High Standard

High Standard Sentinel

High Standard Sentinel
Caliber: 22 short, long, long rifle
Action: Single or double; solid frame
Cylinder: 9-shot swing out; simultaneous manual ejector
Barrel: 3", 4", or 6"
Finish: Blued or nickel; checkered plastic grips; aluminum alloy frame
Estimated Value: $95.00 - $120.00

High Standard Sentinel Deluxe
Same as Sentinel except: adjustable rear sight; checkered square butt walnut grips; wide trigger; 4" or 6" barrel
Estimated Value: $100.00 - $125.00

High Standard Sentinel Deluxe

High Standard Sentinel Snub

High Standard Sentinel Imperial
Same as Sentinel except: ramp front sight; black or nickel finish; checkered square butt walnut grips.
Estimated Value: $105.00 - $130.00

High Standard Sentinel Snub
Same as Sentinel except: 2⅜" barrel only; checkered plastic bird's head grip (round butt); some were made in pink, turquoise, & gold colored finish as well as blue & nickel
Estimated Value: $120.00 - $150.00

High Standard Sentinel New Model

High Standard Sentinel New Model
Similar to the Sentinel with 22 caliber cylinder & interchangeable 22 magnum cylinder. Available with 2" or 4" barrel; add $20.00 for extra cylinder
Estimated Value: $135.00 - $175.00

Revolvers

High Standard Sentinel Mark I
Caliber: 22 short, long, long rifle
Action: Single or double; solid frame
Cylinder: 9-shot swing out; simultaneous manual ejector
Barrel: 2" or 4"
Finish: Blued or nickel; smooth walnut grips; improved all steel version of the 22 caliber Sentinel; add $10.00 for nickel finish
Estimated Value: $120.00 - $160.00

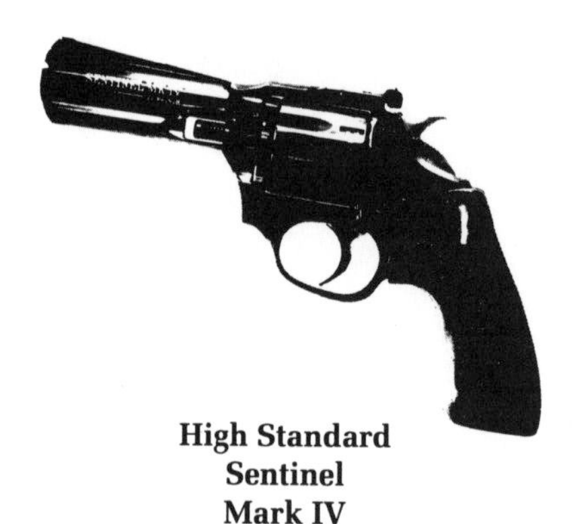

High Standard Sentinel Mark IV

High Standard Sentinel Mark IV
Same as Sentinel Mark I except 22 magnum only; add $10.00 for nickel finish or adjustable rear sight.
Estimated Value: $125.00 - $165.00

High Standard Sentinel Mark III

High Standard Sentinel Mark II
Caliber: 38 Special, 357 magnum
Action: Single or double; solid frame
Cylinder: 6-shot swing out; simultaneous manual ejector
Barrel: 2½", 4", or 6"
Finish: Blued; checkered walnut grips
Estimated Value: $135.00 - $180.00

High Standard Sentinel Mark III
Same as Sentinel Mark II except deluxe trophy blue finish; checkered walnut wrap-around grips; checkered back strap
Estimated Value: $140.00 - $190.00

High Standard Double Nine
Caliber: 22 short, long, long rifle
Action: Single or double; solid frame
Cylinder 9-shot swing out; simultaneous manual ejector
Barrel: 5½"; dummy ejector housing under barrel
Finish: Blued or nickel; plastic grips; aluminum alloy or steel frame; add $10.00 for nickel finish
Estimated Value: $130.00 - $175.00

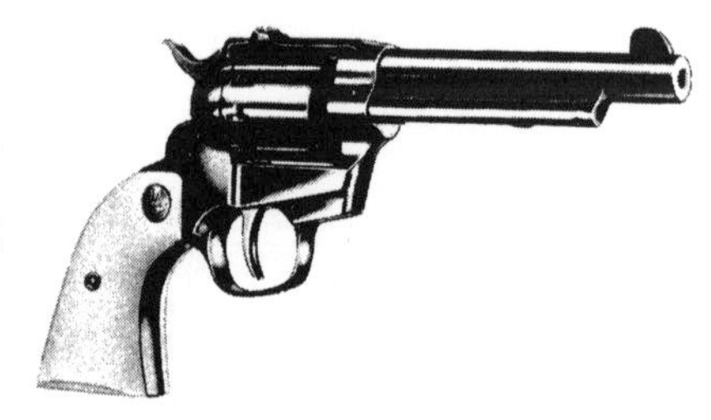

High Standard Double Nine

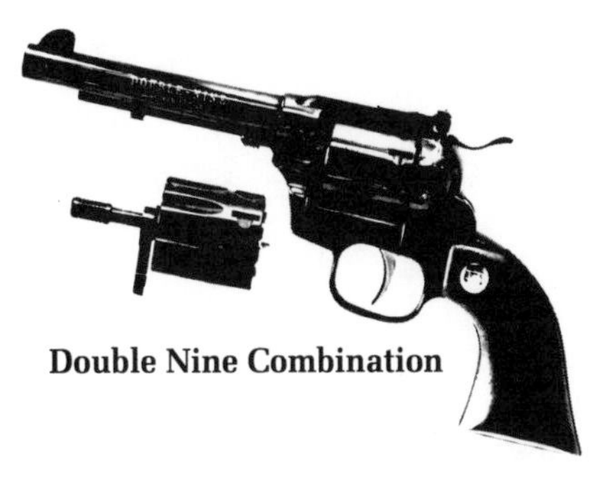
Double Nine Combination

High Standard Double Nine Combination
Same as Double Nine except: extra interchangeable cylinder in 22 magnum caliber; smooth walnut grip; steel frame; add $10.00 for nickel finish
Estimated Value: $140.00 - $190.00

High Standard Natchez
Similar to Double Nine except: 4½" barrel only; blued finish only; plastic ivory bird's head grips
Estimated Value: $110.00 - $150.00

High Standard Natchez

High Standard Posse
Similar to Double Nine except: 3½" barrel without dummy ejector housing; brass trigger guard & grip frame; blued finish only; smooth walnut grips
Estimated Value: $110.00 - $140.00

High Standard Longhorn
Caliber: 22 short, long, long rifle
Action: Single or double; solid frame
Cylinder: 9-shot swing out; simultaneous manual ejector
Barrel: 4½", 5½", or 9½" ; dummy ejector housing under barrel
Finish: Blued; plastic grips; walnut grips on 9½" barrel model; aluminum alloy or steel frame
Estimated Value: $130.00 - $175.00

High Standard Longhorn Combination
Similar to Longhorn except; extra interchangeable cylinder in 22 magnum caliber; 9½" barrel only; smooth walnut grips
Estimated Value: $140.00 - $190.00

High Standard Longhorn

Revolvers

High Standard Kit Gun
Caliber: 22 short, long, long rifle
Action: Single or double; solid frame
Cylinder: 9-shot swing out; simultaneous manual ejector
Barrel: 4"
Finish: Blued; checkered walnut grips; aluminum alloy frame
Estimated Value: $105.00 - $130.00

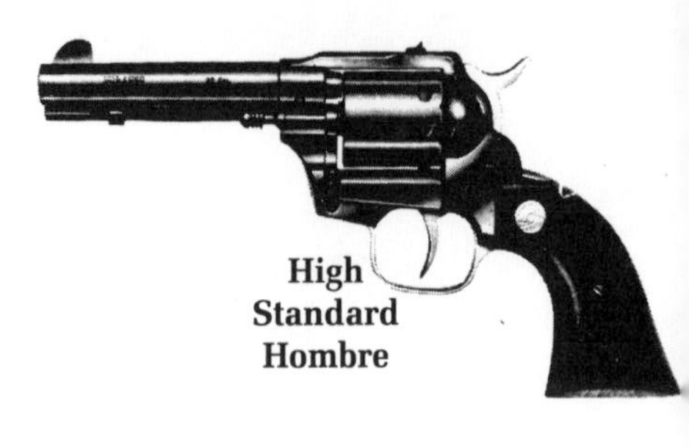

High Standard Hombre

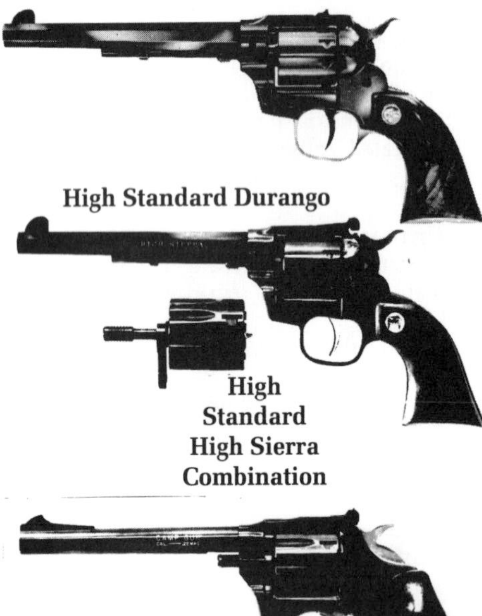

High Standard Durango

High Standard High Sierra Combination

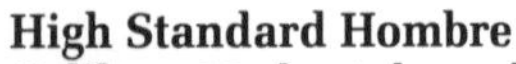

High Standard Hombre
Caliber: 22 short, long, long rifle
Action: Single or double; solid frame
Cylinder: 9-shot swing out; simultaneous ejector
Barrel: 4½"
Finish: Blued or nickel; steel frame; smooth walnut grip; add $5.00 for nickel finish
Estimated Value: $105.00 - $140.00

High Standard Durango
Caliber: 22 short, long, long rifle
Action: Single or double; solid frame
Cylinder: 9-shot swing out; simultaneous ejector
Barrel: 4½" or 5½"; dummy ejector housing under barrel
Finish: Blued or nickel; smooth walnut grip; add $5.00 for nickel
Estimated Value: $115.00 - $150.00

High Standard Camp Gun

High Standard High Sierra Combination
Caliber: 22 short, long, long rifle, & 22 magnum
Action: Single or double; solid frame
Cylinder: 9-shot swing out; interchangable cylinders (22 cal. and 22 magnum cal.)
Barrel: 7" octagonal
Finish: Blued; smooth walnut grip; steel frame; gold plated trigger guard & backstrap
Estimated Value: $140.00 - $190.00

High Standard Camp Gun
Caliber: 22 short, long, long rifle, and 22 mag.; add $3.00 for 22 mag.
Action: Single or double; solid frame; simultaneous ejector
Cylinder: 9-shot swing out
Barrel: 6"
Finish: Blued; checkered walnut grip
Estimated Value: $140.00 - $190.00

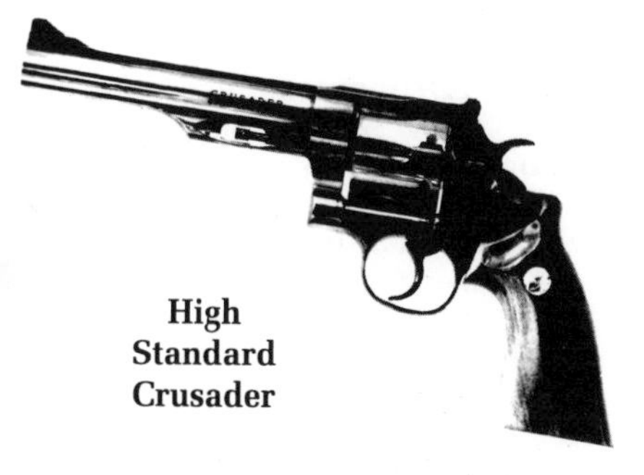

High Standard Crusader

High Standard Crusader
Caliber: 44 mag., 45 Colt, 357 mag.
Action: Single or double
Cylinder: 6-shot
Barrel: 4½", 6½", or 8⅜"; add $5.00 for 6½" barrel; add $12.00 for 8⅜" barrel
Finish: Blued; shrouded ejector rod; smooth walnut grips in 44; checkered walnut grips in 45 & 357
Estimated Value: $240.00 - $300.00

High Standard Crusader Medium Frame

High Standard Crusader Medium Frame
Similar to the Crusader in 357 magnum only; 4½" or 6½" barrel; a smaller version of the Crusader; add $7.00 for 6½" barrel
Estimated Value: $220.00 - $275.00

Iver Johnson

Iver Johnson Safety Hammer
Caliber: 22-short, long, long rifle, 32 S&W, 32 S&W long, or 38 S&W
Action: Single or double; exposed hammer; hinged frame; top break; simultaneous ejector; heavier frame for 32 & 38 calibers
Cylinder: 7-shot in 22 caliber; 6-shot in 32 caliber; 5-shot in 38 caliber
Barrel: 2", 3", 3¼", 4", 5", or 6"; round barrel with rib
Finish: Blued or nickel; hard rubber or wood grips; round or square butt grip
Estimated Value: $95.00 - $120.00

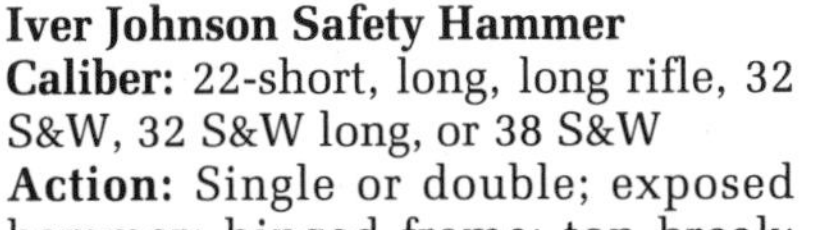

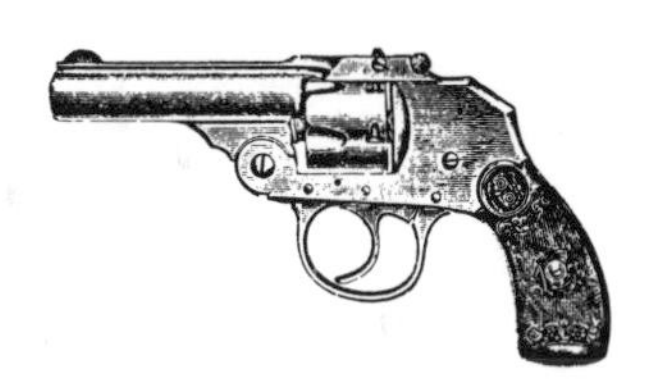

Iver Johnson Safety Hammerless

Iver Johnson Safety Hammer

Iver Johnson Safety Hammerless
Same as Safety Hammer model except: frame extended to enclose hammer; double action only
Estimated Value: $100.00 - $125.00

Iver Johnson Model 1900

Iver Johnson Model 1900
Caliber: 22 short, long, long rifle, 32 S&W, 32 S&W long, 38 S&W
Action: Single or double; exposed hammer; solid frame; side load
Cylinder: 7-shot in 22 caliber; 6-shot in 32 caliber; 5-shot in 38 caliber
Barrel: 2½", 4½", or 6"; octagon barrel
Finish: Blued or nickel; hard rubber grips
Estimated Value: $85.00 - $110.00

Iver Johnson Model 1900 Target
Same as Model 1900 except: 22 caliber only; 6" or 9" barrel; checkered walnut grips; blued finish only
Estimated Value: $ 95.00 - $120.00

Iver Johnson Target 9-Shot Revolver
Similar to Model 1900 Target except 9-shot cylinder; 6" or 10" barrel
Estimated Value: $ 95.00 - $115.00

Iver Johnson Sealed Eight Supershot

Iver Johnson Sealed Eight Target

Iver Johnson Supershot
Caliber: 22 short, long, long rifle
Action: Single or double; exposed hammer; top break style; simultaneous ejector
Cylinder: 7-shot; 9-shot
Barrel: 6"; round barrel with solid rib on top
Finish: Blued; checkered walnut grips (one piece); some have adjustable finger rest behind trigger guard
Estimated Value: $100.00 - $130.00

Iver Johnson Sealed Eight Target
Caliber: 22 short, long, long rifle
Action: Single or double; exposed hammer; solid frame; side load
Cylinder: 8-shot; cylinder recessed for cartridge heads
Barrel: 6", 10"; octagon barrel
Finish: Blued; checkered walnut grips (one piece)
Estimated Value: $100.00 - $125.00

Iver Johnson Sealed Eight Supershot
Similar to Supershot Revolver except: 8-shot cylinder recessed for cartridge heads; 10" barrel
Estimated Value: $115.00 - $140.00

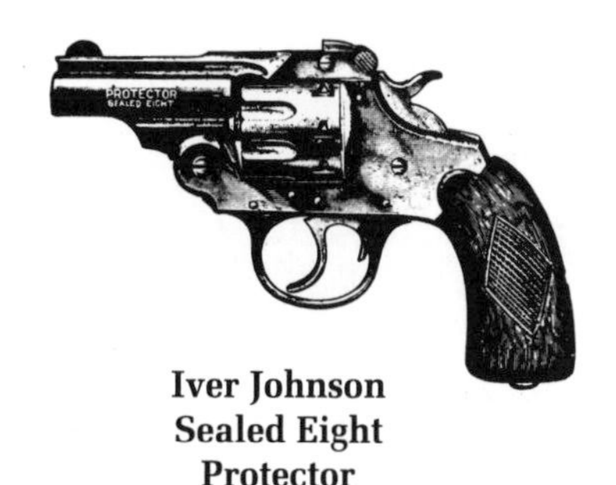

Iver Johnson Sealed Eight Protector

Iver Johnson Sealed Eight Protector
Caliber: 22 short, long, long rifle
Action: Single or double; exposed hammer; hinged top break style; simultaneous ejector
Cylinder: 8-shot; cylinder recessed for cartridge heads
Barrel: 2½" round with solid rib
Finish: Blued; checkered walnut grips; some had adjustable finger rest behind trigger guard
Estimated Value: $105.00 - $140.00

Iver Johnson Champion
Caliber: 22 short, long, long rifle
Action: Single; exposed hammer; hinged frame; top break style; simultaneous ejector
Cylinder: 8-shot; cylinder recessed for cartridge heads
Barrel: 6"
Finish: Blued; checkered walnut grips (one piece); adjustable finger rest behind trigger guard
Estimated Value: $110.00 - $150.00

Iver Johnson Champion

Iver Johnson Trigger Cocking Target
Same as Champion Revolver except the trigger cocks the hammer on the first pull, then releases the hammer to fire the revolver on the second pull
Estimated Value: $120.00 - $160.00

Iver Johnson Trigger Cocking Target

Iver Johnson Armsworth Model 855

Iver Johnson Armsworth Model 855
Caliber: 22 short, long, long rifle
Action: Single; exposed hammer; hinged frame; top break style; simultaneous ejector
Cylinder: 8-shot; cylinder recessed for cartridge heads
Barrel: 6"
Finish: Blued; checkered walnut grips (one piece); adjustable finger rest behind trigger guards.
Estimated Value: $105.00 - $135.00

Iver Johnson Supershot Model 844
Similar to Armsworth Model 855 except double & single action; 4½" or 6" barrel lengths
Estimated Value: $105.00 - $135.00

Iver Johnson Model 55S Cadet

Iver Johnson Model 55S Cadet
Caliber: 22 short, long, long rifle, 32, 38
Action: Single or double; solid frame; exposed hammer; side load
Cylinder: 8-shot in 22 caliber; 5-shot in 32 & 38 calibers; removable cylinder
Barrel: 2½"
Finish: Blued; plastic round butt grips
Estimated Value: $90.00 - $115.00

Iver Johnson Model 55 S-A Cadet

Iver Johnson Model 55 S-A Cadet
Similar to Model 55S Cadet except: loading gate; also in caliber 22 WMR
Estimated Value: $85.00 - $110.00

Iver Johnson Model 55
Caliber: 22 short, long, long rifle
Action: Single or double; exposed hammer; solid frame; side load
Cylinder: 8-shot; chambers recessed for cartridge heads; removable unfluted cylinder
Barrel: 4½" or 6"
Finish: Blued; checkered walnut grips
Estimated Value: $75.00 - $100.00

Iver Johnson Model 57A

Iver Johnson Model 55A Target
Same as Model 55 Revolver except: fluted cylinder; loading gate; checkered plastic grips
Estimated Value: $85.00 - $110.00

Iver Johnson Model 57A Target
Same as Model 55 Revolver except: fluted cylinder; adjustable front and rear sights; checkered plastic grips; loading gate
Estimated Value: $95.00 - $120.00

Iver Johnson Model 57
Same as Model 55 Revolver except: adjustable front and rear sights; checkered plastic grips
Estimated Value: $90.00 - $115.00

Iver Johnson Model 50A Sidewinder

Iver Johnson Model 50A Sidewinder
Caliber: 22 short, long, long rifle
Action: Single or double; exposed hammer; solid frame; side load with loading gate; removable cylinder
Cylinder: 8-shot; recessed chambers
Barrel: 4½", 6"; ejector rod under barrel
Finish: Blued; plastic grips
Estimated Value: $ 90.00 - $110.00

Iver Johnson Model 50A Sidewinder Convertible
Same as Model 50A Sidewinder except: extra interchangeable cylinder for 22 magnum (WMR) cartridges; add $10.00 for adjustable sights
Estimated Value: $95.00 - $120.00

Iver Johnson Model 66 Trailsman
Caliber: 22 short, long, long rifle; 32 S&W, 38 S&W
Action: Single or double; exposed hammer; hinged frame; top break style; simultaneous manual ejector under barrel; rebounding type hammer
Cylinder: 8-shot in 22 caliber; 5-shot in 32 & 38 caliber; chambers recessed for cartridge heads
Barrel: 2¾" or 6", rib on top of barrel
Finish: Blued; checkered walnut or plastic grip; round butt on 2¾" barrel; square butt on 6" barrel
Estimated Value: $ 90.00 - $110.00

Iver Johnson Model 66 Trailsman

Iver Johnson Model 67S Viking

Iver Johnson Model 67S Viking
Same as Model 67 except: 2¾" barrel length
Estimated Value: $105.00 - $130.00

Iver Johnson Model 67 Viking
Same as Model 66 Trailsman except: hammer safety device; 4½" or 6" barrel lengths
Estimated Value: $100.00 - $125.00

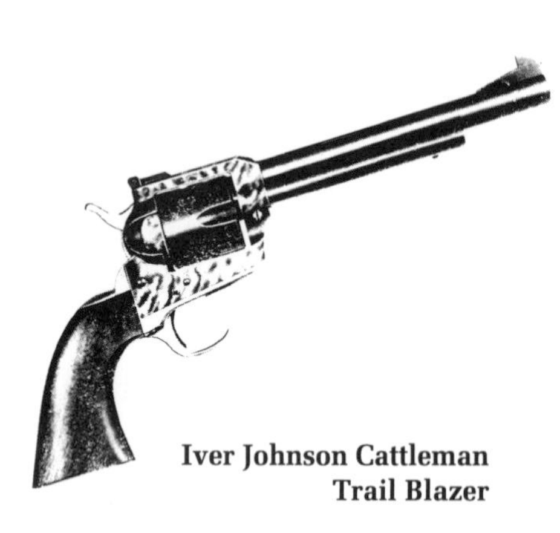

Iver Johnson Cattleman Trail Blazer

Iver Johnson Bulldog
Caliber: 22 short, long, long rifle; 38 Special
Action: Single or double; exposed hammer; solid frame; side load with loading gate
Cylinder: 8-shot in 22 caliber; 5-shot in 38 caliber recessed chambers
Barrel: 2½" or 4", heavy duty ribbed
Finish: Blued; plastic grips; round or square butt ; add $10.00 for 38 caliber
Estimated Value: $90.00 - $115.00

Iver Johnson Cattleman Trail Blazer
Caliber: 22 short, long, long rifle; 22 magnum (WMR)
Action: Single action; solid frame; exposed hammer; side load with loading gate
Cylinder: 6-shot; 2 interchangeable cylinders
Barrel: 5½" or 6"; manual ejector rod under barrel
Finish: Blued; case-hardened frame, brass backstrap & trigger guard; smooth walnut grip
Estimated Value: $145.00 - $180.00

Iver Johnson Cattleman Magnum
Caliber: 38 Special & 357 mag., 45 long Colt, 44 Special & 44 mag.
Action: Single; solid frame; exposed hammer; side load with loading gate
Cylinder: 6-shot
Barrel: 4¾", 5½", 7½" (357 magnum & 45 LC); 4¾", 6", 7½" (44 magnum); manual ejector rod under barrel
Finish: Blued; case-hardened frame, brass backstrap and trigger guard; smooth walnut grip; add $25.00 for 44 magnum
Estimated Value: $150.00 - $190.00

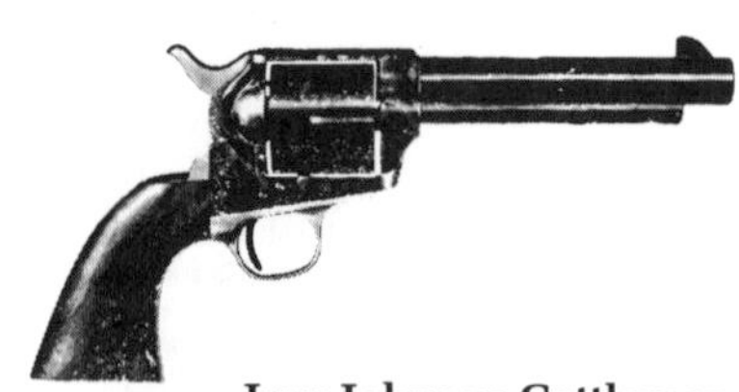

Iver Johnson Cattleman Magnum

Iver Johnson Cattleman Buckhorn Magnum
Same as Cattleman Magnum except: ramp front sight & adjustable rear sight; also 12" barrel; add $25.00 for 12" barrel & $25.00 for 44 magnum.
Estimated Value: $160.00 - $200.00

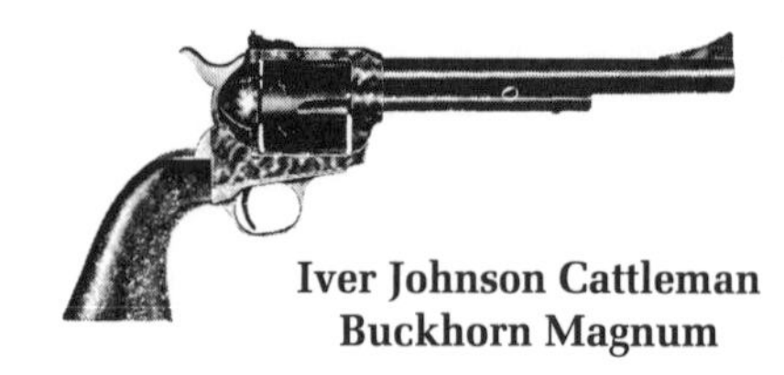

Iver Johnson Cattleman Buckhorn Magnum

Iver Johnson Cattleman Buckhorn Buntline
Same as Cattleman Buckhorn Mag. except 18" barrel only; grip backstrap is cut for shoulder stock attachment; smooth walnut attachable shoulder stock; prices include stock; add $25.00 for 44 mag.
Estimated Value: $280.00 - $350.00

Iver Johnson Cattleman Buckhorn Buntline

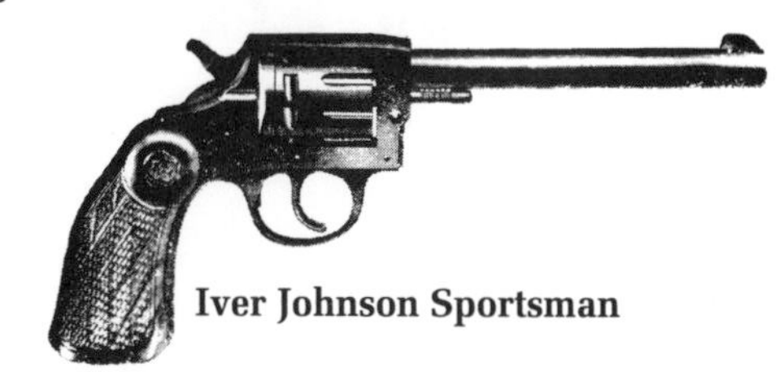

Iver Johnson Sportsman

Iver Johnson Rookie
Caliber: 38 Special
Action: Single or double
Cylinder: 5-shot; fluted
Barrel: 4"
Finish: Blued or nickel; plastic grips
Estimated Value: $100.00 - $130.00

Iver Johnson Sportsman
Similar to the Rookie in 22 long rifle caliber; 4¾" or 6" barrel; blued finish
Estimated Value: $95.00 - $120.00

Iver Johnson Deluxe Target
Similar to the Sportsman with adjustable sights
Estimated Value: $100.00 - $125.00

Llama

Llama Martial

Llama Martial
Caliber: 22 short, long, long rifle; 38 Special
Action: Double action; solid frame; simultaneous ejector
Cylinder: 6-shot swing out with thumb latch on left side of frame
Barrel: 6" in 22 caliber; 4" and 6" in 38 Special; ventilated rib
Finish: Blued, chrome, chrome engraved; checkered wood or simulated pearl grips; add $25.00 for chrome & $25.00 for engraved
Estimated Value: $160.00 - $200.00

Llama Commanche II

Llama Comanche I
Caliber: 22 short, long, long rifle
Action: Double; simultaneous hand ejector; solid frame
Cylinder: 6-shot swing out with thumb latch on left side of frame
Barrel: 6" with ventilated rib
Finish: Blued; checkered walnut target grips; add $25.00 for chrome
Estimated Value: $170.00 - $210.00

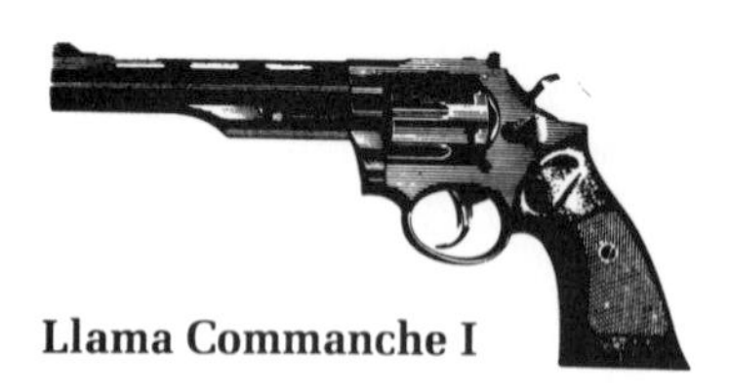
Llama Commanche I

Llama Comanche II
Similar to the Comanche I in 38 Special with a 4" or 6" barrel
Estimated Value: $170.00 - $210.00

Llama Comanche III
Similar to the Comanche II except: 357 magnum; add 17% for satin chrome finish
Estimated Value: $200.00 - $255.00

Llama Super Comanche, Super Comanche IV
A heavier version of the Comanche, for 44 magnum cartridges; 6" barrel or 8½" barrel
Estimated Value: $265.00 - $330.00

Llama Super Comanche V
Similar to the Super Comanche IV except: 357 magnum; 4", 6", or 8½" barrel
Estimated Value: $250.00 - $310.00

New England

New England Ultra Revolver
Caliber: 22 short, long, long rifle; 22 Win. magnum; 32 H&R magnum
Action: Single or double; exposed hammer; swing out cylinder
Cylinder: 9-shot; (reg 22.); 6-shot (22 magnum); 5-shot (32 H&R magnum); simultaneous manual ejector
Barrel: 3" or 6" with solid rib
Finish: Blued; hardwood, walnut finish smooth grips
Estimated Value: $110.00 - $135.00

New England Ultra Revolver

New England Standard Revolver-22
Caliber: 22 short, long, or long rifle; 22 Win. magnum
Action: Single or double; exposed hammer; solid frame
Cylinder: 9-shot in regular 22 cal.; 6-shot in 22 magnum; swing-out, simultaneous manual ejector
Barrel: 2½" or 4"
Finish: Blued or nickel; hardwood, walnut finish smooth grips; add 10% for nickel finish
Estimated Value: $ 80.00 - $100.00

New England Standard Revolver-32 H&R Magnum

New England Standard Revolver-32 H&R Magnum
Same as the Standard Revolver-22 except 32 H&R magnum caliber only; 5-shot cylinder; add 10% for nickel finish
Estimated Value: $80.00 - $100.00

North American Arms

North American Arms (Mini Revolver)
Caliber: 22 short or 22 long rifle ; 22 magnum
Action: Single action; exposed hammer; spur trigger; solid frame
Cylinder: 5-shot; removable cylin-der; available with two cylin-ders (22 long rifle and 22 magnum)
Barrel: 1⅛", 1⅝", or 2½"
Finish: Stainless steel; polycarbonate round butt (bird head) grips; add 16% for 22 magnum, 38% for revolver with both cylinders, and 10% for 2½" barrel
Estimated Value: $100.00 - $120.00

North American Arms (Mini Revolver)

Ruger

Ruger Single-Six
Caliber: 22 short, long, & long rifle; 22 WMR
Action: Single; solid frame with loading gate
Cylinder: 6-shot half fluted
Barrel: 4⅝", 5½", 6½", or 9½"; ejector rod under barrel
Finish: Blued; checkered hard rubber or smooth walnut grips; add $150.00 for flat loading gate
Estimated Value: $160.00 - $200.00

Ruger New Model Super Single-Six Convertible

Ruger Lightweight Single-Six
Same as Ruger Single-Six except: made in 22 short, long, & long rifle only; 4⅝" barrel; cylinder & frame made of lightweight alloy
Estimated Value: $180.00 - $225.00

Ruger Convertible Single-Six
Same as Ruger Single-Six revolver except: furnished with two cylinders – one chambered for regular 22 & the other chambered for 22 WMR
Estimated Value: $175.00 - $220.00

Stainless Steel Ruger New Model Super Single-Six Convertible

Ruger Convertible Super Single-Six
Same as Ruger Single-six revolver except: ramp front sight; adjustable rear sight with protective ribs; priced for gun with both cylinders
Estimated Value: $180.00 - $225.00

Ruger New Model Super Single-Six Convertible
Similar to Ruger Convertible Super Single-Six except: improved version featuring wide trigger; heavy stronger lock words; transfer bar firing pin protector; new interlocking mechanism; other improvements; priced with 22 LR and 22 WMR cylinders
Estimated Value: $170.00 - $210.00

Ruger New Model Super Single-Six Convertible Stainless Steel
Same as Ruger New Model Super Single-Six Convertible Revolver except: stainless steel; 5½" or 6½" barrel; priced for gun with both cylinders
Estimated Value: $215.00 - $265.00

Ruger New Model Single-Six 32 Mag

Ruger New Model Single-Six 32 Mag
Caliber: 32 H&R magnum, also handles 32 S&W & 32 S&W long
Action: Single; solid frame with loading gate
Cylinder: 6-shot, heavy fluted cylinder
Barrel: 4¾", 5½", 6½", or 9½"; ejector rod under barrel
Finish: Blued; smooth walnut grips
Estimated Value: $165.00 - $200.00

Ruger Blackhawk 357 Magnum
Caliber: 357 magnum & 38 Special interchangeably
Action: Single; solid frame with loading gate
Cylinder: 6-shot
Barrel: 4⅝", 6½"; round barrel with ejector rod under barrel
Finish: Blued; checkered hard rubber or smooth walnut wood grips; in 1961 the frame was made heavier with ribs to protect the rear sight and a slight grip modification
Estimated Value:
Pre-1961: $150.00 - $210.00
Post-1961: $175.00 - $240.00

Ruger Blackhawk 357 Convertible
Same as Ruger Blackhawk 357 Magnum except: fitted with extra interchangeable cylinder for 9mm Parabellum cartridges
Estimated Value: $180.00 - $225.00

Ruger Blackhawk 357 Convertible

Ruger New Model Blackhawk 357

Ruger New Model Blackhawk
Similar to Ruger Blackhawk 357 mag. except: improvments featuring wide trigger; stronger lock works; transfer bar firing pin protector, new interlocking mechanism; other improvements. made in 30 carbine, 357 mag., 41 mag. & 45 long Colt; deduct 4% for 30 carbine; add 5% for stainless steel 45 long Colt.
Estimated Value: $195.00 - $245.00

Ruger New Model Blackhawk Convertible
Same as Ruger New Model Blackhawk except: fitted with extra interchangeable cylinders for 357 mag. & 9mm Parabellum cartridges; 45 Colt & 45 ACP cartridges; blued finish
Estimated Value: $205.00 - $255.00

Ruger Super Blackhawk 44 Magnum

Ruger Stainless Steel New Model Blackhawk 357
Same as Ruger New Model Blackhawk except: stainless steel; 357 magnum cal.
Estimated Value: $240.00 - $300.00

Ruger Blackhawk 44 Magnum
Caliber: 44 magnum & 44 S&W Special interchangeably
Action: Single; solid frame with loading gate
Cylinder: 6-shot; heavy fluted cylinder
Barrel: 6½"; ejector rod under barrel
Finish: Blued; smooth walnut grips
Estimated Value: $250.00 - $300.00

Ruger Super Blackhawk 44 Magnum
Caliber: 44 magnum & 44 S&W Special interchangeably
Action: Single; solid frame with loading gate
Cylinder: 6-shot; heavy non-fluted cylinder
Barrel: 7½"; ejector rod under barrel
Finish: Blued; smooth walnut wood grips; square back trigger guard
Estimated Value: $200.00 - $250.00

Ruger New Model Super Blackhawk44 Magnum

Ruger New Model Super Blackhawk 44 Magnum
Similar to Super Blackhawk except: improvments featuring stronger lock works; transfer bar firing pin protector; new interlocking mechanism; blued or stainless steel; 5½", 7½", or 10½" barrel; other improvements; add 10% for stainless steel
Estimated Value: $225.00 - $285.00

Ruger Blackhawk 45 Caliber
Caliber: 45 long Colt
Action: Single; solid frame with loading gate
Cylinder: 6-shot
Barrel: 4⅝", 7½" round barrel with ejector rod under barrel
Finish: Blued; smooth walnut grips; replaced by new model blackhawk in 1973
Estimated Value: $175.00 - $220.00

Ruger Blackhawk 45 Caliber Convertible
Same as Blackhawk 45 Caliber except: fitted with extra interchangeable cylinder for 45 ACP cartridges; replaced by New Model Blackhawk in 1973
Estimated Value: $200.00 - $250.00

Ruger Blackhawk 41 Magnum
Caliber: 41 magnum
Action: Single; solid frame with loading gate
Cylinder: 6-shot
Barrel: 4⅝", 6½" with ejector rod
Finish: Blued; smooth walnut grips
Estimated Value: $190.00 - $240.00

Ruger Blackhawk 41 Magnum

Ruger Blackhawk 30 Caliber
Caliber: 30 U.S. Carbine (M1)
Action: Single; solid frame with loading gate
Cylinder: 6-shot
Barrel: 7½" with ejector rod
Finish: Blued; smooth walnut wood grips; a good companion handgun for the M1 carbine
Estimated Value: $185.00 - $230.00

Ruger Blackhawk 30 Caliber

Ruger Security-Six 357 Magnum
Caliber: 357 magnum, 38 Special
Action: Double & single; solid frame; exposed hammer
Cylinder: 6-shot; simultaneous ejector
Barrel: 2¾", 4", 6"
Finish: Blued or stainless steel; square butt, checkered walnut grips; a solid frame revolver with swing-out cylinder; add $20.00 for stainless steel
Estimated Value: $180.00 - $225.00

Ruger Speed-Six
Similar to Security-Six 357 Magnum except: round butt style grips & calibers 9mm Parabellum, 38 Special & 357 magnum; add $16.00 for 9mm; add 9% for stainless steel
Estimated Value: $165.00 - $220.00

Ruger Security-Six

Ruger Service-Six, Police Service-Six
Similar to Speed-Six except: square butt style grips; add $16.00 for 9mm; add 8% for stainless steel
Estimated Value: $160.00 - $215.00

Ruger Redhawk

Ruger Redhawk
Caliber: 357 mag., 41 mag., 44 mag.
Action: Double & single; solid frame; exposed hammer
Cylinder: 6-shot swing out; simultaneous ejector
Barrel: 5½", 7½", shrouded ejector rod under barrel
Finish: Blued or Stainless steel; checkered or smooth walnut grips; a heavy frame magnum revolver; add 13% for stainless steel, 8% for scope rings
Estimated Value: $275.00 - $340.00

Ruger New Model Bisley
Caliber: 22 long rifle or 32 H&R mag. in small frame; 357 mag., 41 mag., 44 mag., or 45 long Colt in large frame
Action: Single; solid frame with loading gate
Cylinder: 6-shot fluted or non-fluted cylinder with or without roll engraving
Barrel: 6½" small frame, 7½" large frame; ejector rod under barrel
Finish: Blued; smooth wood grips; Ruger single action design with a different-angle grip, similar to the old Colt Bisley revolvers
Estimated Value:
Small Frame: $195.00 - $245.00
Large Frame: $235.00 - $295.00

Ruger Super Redhawk
Caliber: 44 magnum & 44 Special
Action: Double & single; solid frame; exposed hammer
Cylinder: 6-shot swing out; simultaneous ejector; fluted cylinder
Barrel: 7½" or 9½"
Finish: Stainless steel; cushioned grip system features rubber panels with Goncalo Alves panel inserts
Estimated Value: $350.00 - $440.00

Ruger Bearcat
Caliber: 22 short, long, long rifle
Action: Single; solid frame with loading gate
Cylinder: 6-shot; non-fluted, engraved
Barrel: 4" round with ejector rod
Finish: Blued; smooth walnut grips; alloy frame; coil springs
Estimated Value: $225.00 - $300.00

Ruger Bearcat

Ruger Super Bearcat

Ruger Super Bearcat
Same as Ruger Bearcat except: all steel construction
Estimated Value: $220.00 - $275.00

Ruger GP-100
Double-Action Revolver
Caliber: 357 magnum or 38 Special
Action: Double & single; solid frame; exposed hammer
Cylinder: 6-shot; swing out; simultaneous ejector
Barrel: 4" heavy barrel or 6" with ejector shroud
Finish: Blued or stainless steel; with a new Ruger cushioned grip system; rubber grips with polished wood inserts; add 8% for stainless steel; add 4% for adjustable sights
Estimated Value: $240.00 - $295.00

Ruger GP-100 Double-Action Revolver

Ruger Model SP 101
Caliber: 38 Special, 9mm, 357 mag., 32 H&R, 22 short, long, or long rifle
Action: Single & double; exposed hammer
Cylinder: 5-shot (38 Special, 9mm, and 357 magnum); 6-shot (22 & 32 H&R caliber); swing-out
Barrel: 2" or 3 1/16" (38 Special); 2" or 4" (22 caliber) with ejector rod shroud
Finish: Stainless steel; grips are rubber with polished wood inserts
Estimated Value: $245.00 - $305.00

Smith & Wesson

Smith & Wesson No. 3
Single Action New Model
Caliber: 44 S&W Russian center fire
Action: Single; exposed hammer; hinged frame (top break); simultaneous automatic ejector
Cylinder: 6-shot
Barrel: 4", 5", 6", 6½", or 7½"; ribbed
Finish: Blued or nickel; round butt, hard rubber or checkered walnut grips; sometimes called Single Action Russian Model
Estimated Value: $720.00 - $900.00

Smith & Wesson No. 3 Single Action New Model

Smith & Wesson No. 3 New Model Double Action
Same as No. 3 Single Action New Model except: double & single action; 4", 5", 6", or 6½" barrel; sometimes listed as S&W 1881 Navy; rear of trigger guard is square
Estimated Value: $400.00 - $500.00

Smith & Wesson No. 3 New Model Double Action

Smith & Wesson Double Action 44 Wesson Favorite
Similar to No. 3 Single Action New Model except: double & single action; 5" barrel only; lighter barrel & frame; (approximately 1,200 produced)
Estimated Value: $1,200.00 - $1,800.00

Smith & Wesson 38 Double Action
Caliber: 38 S&W
Action: Single & double; exposed hammer; hinged frame; top break; back of trigger guard squared
Cylinder: 5-shot; simultaneous ejector
Barrel: 3¼", 4", 5", 6"
Finish: Blued or nickel; round butt; hard rubber grips
Estimated Value: $360.00 - $450.00

Smith & Wesson 32 Double Action
Caliber: 32 S&W center fire
Action: Single & double; exposed hammer; hinged frame (top break)
Cylinder: 5-shot; simultaneous ejector
Barrel: 3" 1880-1882; 3", 3½", 6", 8", 10" 1882-1909; 3", 3½", 6" 1909-1919
Finish: Blued or nickel; round butt, hard rubber grips; rear of trigger guard is square; made in five modifications or issues

Issue	Dates	Quantity	Value
1st	1880	*under* 100	$2,000.00-$2,500.00
2nd	1880-1882	22,000	$200.00 - $230.00
3rd	1882-1889	21,200	$205.00 - $235.00
4th	1889-1909	239,500	$150.00 - $180.00
5th	1909-1919	44,600	$175.00 - $200.00

Smith & Wesson 38 Double Action

Smith & Wesson Safety Model Double Action
Caliber: 32 S&W, 38 S&W
Action: Double only; concealed hammer enclosed by frame; hinged frame; top break style; grip safety on rear of grip frame
Cylinder: 5-shot; simultaneous ejector
Barrel: 2", 3", or 3½" in 32 caliber; 2", 3¼", 4", 5", or 6" in 38 caliber; ribbed
Finish: Blued or nickel; hard rubber or checkered walnut grips; sometimes listed as the Safety Hammerless, New Department Model
Estimated Value: $300.00 - $375.00

Smith & Wesson Perfected 38
Caliber: 38 S&W center fire
Action: Single & double; exposed hammer; hinged frame (top break; but also has side latch)
Cylinder: 5-shot; simultaneous ejector
Barrel: 3¼", 4", 5", & 6"
Finish: Blued or nickel; round butt, hard rubber grip
Estimated Value: $385.00 - $300.00

Smith & Wesson Single Action Target
Caliber: 32-44 S&W, 38-44 S&W
Action: Single; exposed hammer; hinged frame (top break)
Cylinder: 6-shot; simultaneous ejector
Barrel: 6½"
Finish: Blued or nickel; round butt; hard rubber or checkered walnut grips
Estimated Value: $560.00 - $700.00

Smith & Wesson No. 3 Single Action Frontier
Caliber: 44-40 Winchester rifle cartridge
Action: Single; exposed hammer; hinged frame (top break)
Cylinder: 6-shot; simultaneous automatic ejector
Barrel: 4", 5", or 6½"
Finish: Blued or nickel; round butt, hard rubber or checkered walnut grips
Estimated Value: $800.00 - $1,000.00

Smith & Wesson Double Action Frontier
Similar to No. 3 Single Action Frontier except: double & single action; rear of trigger guard is square
Estimated Value: $480.00 - $600.00

Smith & Wesson 1891 Single Action
Caliber: 38 S&W center fire
Action: Single; exposed hammer; hinged frame (top break)
Cylinder: 5-shot; simultaneous ejector
Barrel: 3¼", 4", 5", or 6"
Finish: Blued or nickel; round butt, hard rubber grips; this revolver was also made with an accessory single shot target barrel in 22 caliber, 32 caliber, or 38 caliber in 6", 8" or 10" lengths; add 75% for revolver with extra single shot barrel
Estimated Value: $450.00 - $560.00

Smith & Wesson 1891 Single Action

Smith & Wesson Model M Hand Ejector

Smith & Wesson Model M Hand Ejector
Caliber: 22 short, long, long rifle
Action: Double & single; exposed hammer; solid frame
Cylinder: 9-shot; swing out, simultaneous manual ejector
Barrel: 2¼", 3", 3½", or 6"
Sights: Fixed or adjustable (available after 1911)
Finish: Blued or nickel; checkered hard rubber round or square butt grips; cylinder latch release on left side of frame or under barrel; sometimes called "Lady Smith"
Estimated Value: $600.00 - $725.00

Smith & Wesson Model 1 Hand Ejector
Caliber: 32 S&W long
Action: single & double; exposed hammer; first Smith & Wesson solid frame revolver; longer top strap over cylinder than later models
Cylinder: 6-shot; swing out; simultaneous manual ejector
Barrel: 3¼", 4¼", or 6"
Finish: Blued or nickel; round butt; hard rubber grips
Estimated Value: $320.00 - $400.00

Smith & Wesson 1899 Hand Ejector
Caliber: 38 long Colt
Action: Double & single; exposed hammer; solid frame
Cylinder: 6-shot; swing out; simultaneous manual ejector; cylinder release on side of frame
Barrel: 4", 5", 6", or 6½"
Finish: Blued or nickel; checkered hard rubber or walnut round butt grips; made for police, Army, Navy, & commercial use; Army & Navy versions have lanyard swivel in butt & 6" or 6½" barrel
Estimated Value: $440.00 - $550.00

Smith & Wesson Military & Police Winchester 32-20
Similar to Model 1899 except: caliber 32-20 only; some improvements & changes
Estimated Value: $250.00 - $320.00

Smith & Wesson Model 30 Hand Ejector
Caliber: 32 S&W & 32 S&W long
Action: Single & double; exposed hammer; solid frame
Cylinder: 6-shot swing out; simultaneous manual ejector; cylinder release on left side of frame
Barrel: 2", 3", 4", or 6"
Finish: Blued or nickel; checkered hard rubber or checkered walnut round butt grips
Estimated Value: $170.00 - $225.00

Smith & Wesson 44 Hand Ejector
Similar to New Century Triple Lock except: cylinder crane lock eliminated; calibers 44 Smith & Wesson Special, 44 Smith & Wesson Russian, or 45 Colt; 45 Colt caliber made in 6½" barrel only; other calibers in 4", 5", or 6" lengths
Estimated Value: $440.00 - $550.00

Smith & Wesson
Model 22/32 Target

Smith & Wesson Model
35 22/32 Target

Smith & Wesson 22/32 Target
Caliber: 22 short, long, long rifle
Action: Single & double; exposed hammer; solid frame
Cylinder: 6-shot swing out; recessed chambers (1935-1953); cylinder release on left side of frame
Barrel: 6"
Finish: Blued; checkered square butt walnut grips; frame design similar to Model 30 hand ejector
Estimated Value: $240.00 - $300.00

Smith & Wesson 22/32 1935 Kit Gun
Same as 22/32 Target except: 4" barrel; round butt grips
Estimated Value: $210.00 - $270.00

Smith & Wesson
Model 35 22/32 Target
Similar to 22/32 target except: target sights; S&W magna-type target grips
Estimated Value: $220.00 - $275.00

Smith & Wesson Model 34 1953 22/32 Kit Gun
Similar to 22/32 Kit Gun except: 2" or 4" barrel; round or square butt grips; blued or nickel finish
Estimated Value: $210.00 - $270.00

Smith & Wesson
New Century Triple Lock
Caliber: 44 S&W Special, 450 Eley, 45 Colt, or 455 Mark II British
Action: Single & double; exposed hammer; solid frame
Cylinder: 6-shot swing out; simultaneous hand ejector; called triple lock because of lock on cylinder crane as well as the usual locks under barrel & at rear of cylinder
Barrel: 4", 5", 6½", or 7½" tapered round
Finish: Blued or nickel; checkered square butt walnut grips
Estimated Value: $575.00 - $675.00

Smith & Wesson Mexican Model
Caliber: 38 S&W center fire
Action: Single; exposed hammer; hinged frame (top break); spur trigger
Cylinder: 5-shot; simultaneous ejector
Barrel: 3¼", 4", 5", or 6"
Finish: Blued or nickel; round butt, hard rubber grips; similar to Model 1891 except: it has a spur trigger; doesn't have half-cock
Estimated Value: $900.00 - $1,200.00

Smith & Wesson Model
34 1953 22/32 Kit Gun

Smith & Wesson Model 51 1960 22/32 Kit Gun

Smith & Wesson
Model 43 1955 22/32 Kit Gun
Same as Model 34 1953 22/32 Kit Gun except: 3½" barrel only; alloy frame; square butt grips
Estimated Value: $210.00 - $260.00

Smith & Wesson
Model 51 1960 22/32 Kit Gun
Same as Model 43 1953 22/32 Kit Gun except: chambered for 22 magnum only; all steel construction
Estimated Value: $220.00 - $275.00

Smith & Wesson 1917 Army
Caliber: 45 auto rim cartridge; 45 ACP (by using two 3 round steel half moon clips to hold the cartridge heads)
Action: Single & double; exposed hammer; solid frame
Cylinder: 6-shot swing out; simultaneous manual ejector; release on left side of frame
Barrel: 5½"
Finish: Blued; smooth or checkered square butt walnut grips
Estimated Value: $275.00 - $350.00

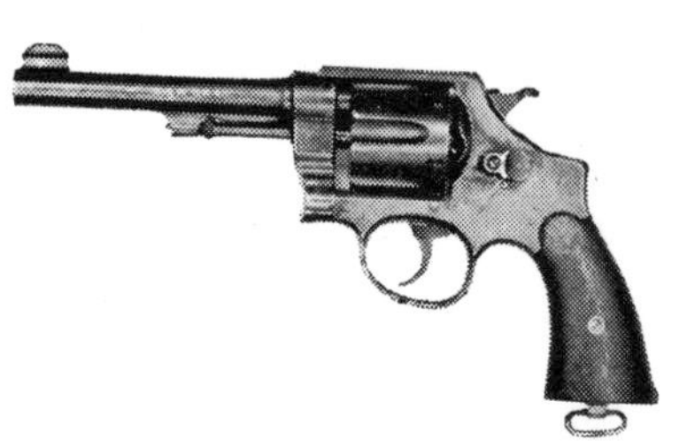

Smith & Wesson 1917 Army

Smith & Wesson
Model 22 1950 Army
Similar to 1917 Army except: made after World War II; minor changes
Estimated Value: $235.00 - $295.00

Smith & Wesson Model 25 45 Colt
Caliber: 45 Colt
Action: Single & double; exposed hammer; solid frame
Cylinder: 6-shot swing out; simultaneous manual ejector; cylinder release on left side
Barrel: 4", 6", or 8⅜"
Finish: Blued or nickel; checkered Goncolo Alves target grips; built on the large N frame; add 3% for 8⅜" barrel; add 9% for presentation case
Estimated Value: $260.00 - $320.00

Smith & Wesson
Model 25 1955 45 Target

Smith & Wesson
Model 25 1955 Target
Similar to the Model 25 45 colt except: 6" barrel only; blued finish; 45 ACP caliber; add 9% for presentation case
Estimated Value: $260.00 - $325.00

Smith & Wesson 1926 Model 44 Military
Caliber: 44 S&W Special
Action: Single & double; exposed hammer
Cylinder: 6-shot swing out; simultaneous manual ejector; cylinder release on left side of frame
Barrel: 3¼", 4", 5", or 6½"
Finish: Blued or nickel; checkered square butt walnut grips
Estimated Value: $360.00 - $450.00

Smith & Wesson 1926 Model 44 Military

Smith & Wesson 1926 Model 44 Target

Smith & Wesson 1926 Model 44 Target
Same as 1926 Model Military except: 6½" barrel only; adjustable target sights; blued finish only
Estimated Value: $400.00 - $500.00

Smith & Wesson Model 21 1950 44 Military

Smith & Wesson Model 24 1950 44 Target

Smith & Wesson Model 21 1950 44 Military
Similar to 1926 Model Military revolver except: made after World War II; minor changes
Estimated Value: $255.00 - $320.00

Smith & Wesson Model 24 1950 44 Target
Similar to 1926 Model 44 Target except: 4" or 6½" barrel; made after World War II; minor changes; ribbed barrel
Estimated Value: $280.00 - $350.00

Smith & Wesson Model 624 44 Special
Similar to the Model 24, 1950 44 Target Revolver except: stainless steel; add 3% for 6½" barrel
Estimated Value: $300.00 - $375.00

Smith & Wesson Model 624

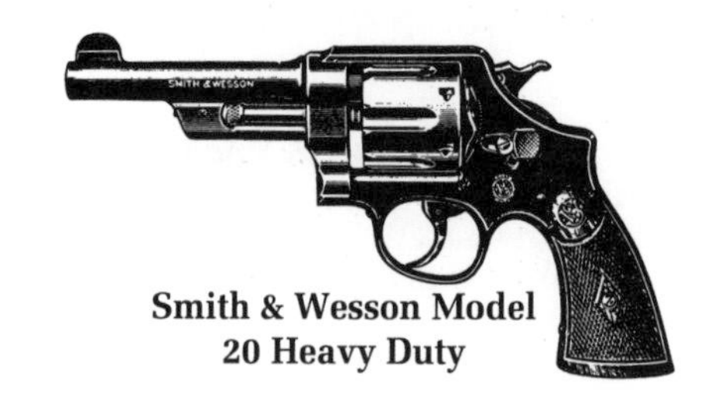
Smith & Wesson Model 20 Heavy Duty

Smith & Wesson
Model 20 Heavy Duty
Caliber: 38 Special
Action: Single & double; exposed hammer; solid frame
Cylinder: 6-shot swing out; simultaneous ejector; release on left side of frame
Barrel: 4", 5", or 6½"
Finish: Blued or nickel; checkered square butt walnut grips
Estimated Value: $280.00 - $350.00

Smith & Wesson Model 23 Outdoorsman

Smith & Wesson
Model 23 Outdoorsman
Similar to Model 20 Heavy Duty except: target version; 6½" barrel only; ribbed barrel after 1950; blued finish; adjustable target sights
Estimated Value: $320.00 - $400.00

Smith & Wesson
Model 10 M&P

Smith & Wesson Military & Police
Caliber: 38 Special
Action: Single & double; exposed hammer; solid frame
Cylinder: 6-shot swing out; simultaneous ejector; release on left side of frame
Barrel: 2" (after 1933); 4", 5", 6", or 6½"
Finish: Blued or nickel; checkered hard rubber or checkered walnut round or square butt grips; basic frame is known as K frame; add $15.00 for nickel finish
Estimated Value: $190.00 - $240.00

Smith & Wesson Model 10 M & P
Caliber: 38 Special
Action: Double & single; exposed hammer; solid frame
Cylinder: 6-shot swing out; simultaneous manual ejector
Barrel: 2", 3", or 4"
Finish: Blued or nickel; square or round butt checkered walnut grips; add 4% for nickel finish
Estimated Value: $210.00 - $260.00

Smith & Wesson Victory Model
Same as Model 10 M & P except: sand blasted or brushed parkerized finish; 4" barrel; smooth square butt grips with lanyard ring; made from about 1941-1946 for the U.S. Government during World War II; 38 Special caliber; Some 38-200 caliber with 5" barrel were made for the British Forces
Estimated Value: $190.00 - $250.00

Smith & Wesson Model 64 M& P
Same as Model 10 M & P except: satin finish stainless steel construction
Estimated Value: $230.00 - $290.00

Smith & Wesson Model 64

Smith & Wesson Model 12 M & P Airweight
Same as Model 10 M & P except: light alloy frame; 2" or 4" barrel
Estimated Value: $190.00 - $250.00

Smith & Wesson Model 13 M&P
Similar to the Model 10 M & P except: 357 magnum caliber with 3" or 4" heavy barrel
Estimated Value: $210.00 - $265.00

Smith & Wesson Model 13

Smith & Wesson Model 65 M&P
Similar to the Model 13 M & P except: satin stainless steel finish
Estimated Value: $230.00 - $290.00

Smith & Wesson Model 12 Military & Police Airweight

Smith & Wesson Model 65 Lady Smith
Similar to the Model 65 M&P except: 3" barrel; round butt rosewood grips; includes soft side Lady Smith case; glass bead finished stainless steel
Estimated Value: $260.00 - $325.00

Smith & Wesson 38 M & P Target
Same as Model 10 M & P except: 6" barrel only; adjustable target sights
Estimated Value: $175.00 - $225.00

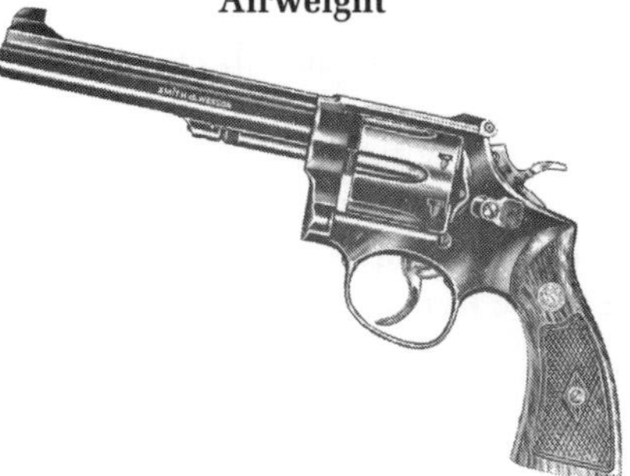

Smith & Wesson K-32 Target

Smith & Wesson K-32 Target
Similar to S&W 38 M & P Target except: caliber 32 S&W, 32 S&W long, & 32 Colt New Police; heavier barrel
Estimated Value: $540.00 - $675.00

Revolvers

Smith & Wesson
Model 31 Regulation Police
Caliber: 32 S&W Long, 32 Colt New Police
Action: Single & double; exposed hammer; solid frame
Cylinder: 6-shot swing out; simultaneous manual ejector; release on left side of frame
Barrel: 2" (after 1949); 3", 3¼", 4", 4¼", or 6"
Finish: Blued or nickel; checkered square butt walnut grips; nickel finish discontinued in early 1980's
Estimated Value: $220.00 - $275.00

Smith & Wesson
Regulation Police Target
Similar to Smith & Wesson Model 31 Regulation Police except: 6" barrel only; adjustable target sights; blued finish
Estimated Value: $190.00 - $240.00

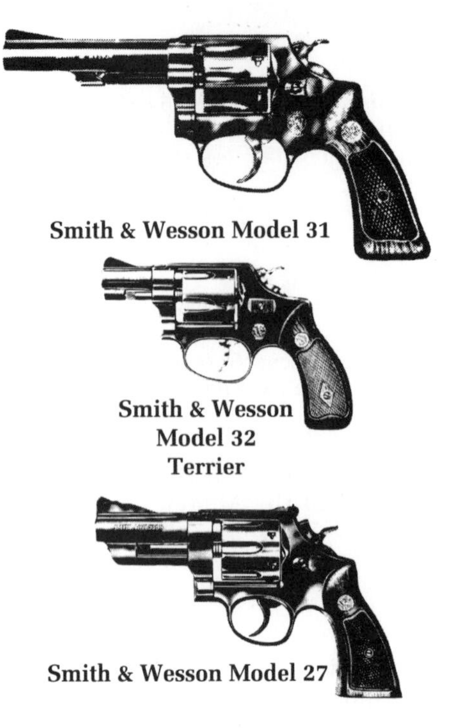
Smith & Wesson Model 31

Smith & Wesson Model 32 Terrier

Smith & Wesson Model 27

Smith & Wesson Model 32 Terrier
Similar to Model 33 Regulation Police except: 2" barrel only
Estimated Value: $175.00 - $215.00

Smith & Wesson Model 33 Regulation Police Revolver
Same as S&W Model 31 Regulation Police except: 38 caliber S&W & 38 Colt New Police; 5-shot cylinder
Estimated Value: $185.00 - $230.00

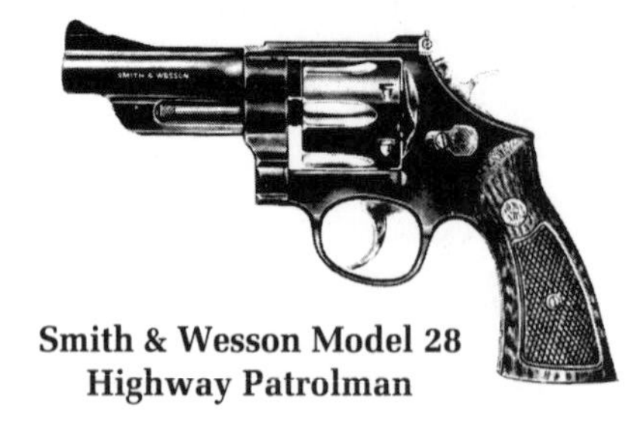
Smith & Wesson Model 28 Highway Patrolman

Smith & Wesson
Model 27 357 Magnum
Caliber: 357 magnum & 38 Special
Action: Single & double; exposed hammer; solid frame
Cylinder: 6-shot swing out; simultaneous manual ejector
Barrel: 3½", 5", 6", 6½", or 8⅜" ribbed; add 2% for 8⅜" barrel
Finish: Blued or nickel; checkered walnut grips
Estimated Value: $265.00 - $330.00

Smith & Wesson
Model 28 Highway Patrolman
Similar to Model 27 357 Magnum except: 4" or 6" barrel; adjustable rear sight; blued finish; add 10% for target grips
Estimated Value: $210.00 - $265.00

Smith & Wesson K-22 Outdoorsman

Smith & Wesson
Model 14 K-38 Masterpiece
Caliber: 38 Special
Action: Single or double; or single action only; exposed hammer; solid frame
Cylinder: 6-shot swing out; simultaneous manual ejector; release on left side of frame
Barrel: 6" or 8⅜"; add $10.00 for 8⅜" barrel
Finish: Blued; checkered square butt walnut grips; add $40.00 for target accessories
Estimated Value: $250.00 - $320.00

Smith & Wesson
Model 16 K-32 Masterpiece
Same as Model 14 K-38 Masterpiece except: 32 S&W long & 32 Colt Police caliber; 6" barrel only; double & single action
Estimated Value: $220.00 - $275.00

Smith & Wesson
Model 14 Single Action
Similar to the Model 14 K-38 Masterpiece except: single action; 6" barrel only
Estimated Value: $195.00 - $245.00

Smith & Wesson Model 15
38 Combat Masterpiece
Same as Model 14 K-38 Masterpiece except: 2", 4", 6", or 8⅜" barrel; blued or nickel finish; double & single action; add 7% for nickel finish & 3% for 8⅜" barrel
Estimated Value: $225.00 - $280.00

Smith & Wesson
Model K-22 Outdoorsman
Caliber: 22 short, long, long rifle
Action: Single & double; exposed hammer; solid frame
Cylinder: 6-shot swing out; simultaneous manual ejector; release on left side of frame
Barrel: 6"
Finish: Blued or nickel; checkered walnut grips
Estimated Value: $240.00 - $300.00

Smith & Wesson K-22 Masterpiece
Same as K-22 Outdoorsman except: improved version; better adjustable rear sight; short cocking action; antibacklash trigger
Estimated Value: $240.00 - $300.00

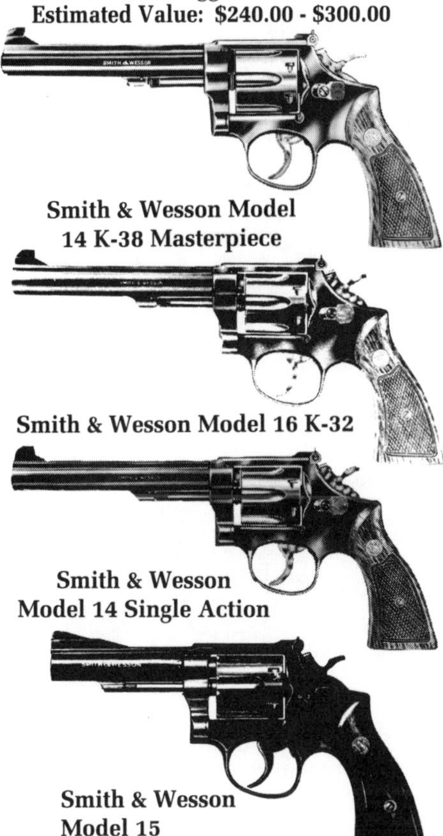

Smith & Wesson Model 14 K-38 Masterpiece

Smith & Wesson Model 16 K-32

Smith & Wesson Model 14 Single Action

Smith & Wesson Model 15

Smith & Wesson Model 67

Smith & Wesson 17 K-22 Masterpiece

Smith & Wesson
Model 67 38 Combat Masterpiece
Same as Model 15 38 combat Masterpiece except: 4" barrel only; satin finish stainless steel
Estimated Value: $250.00 - $315.00

Smith & Wesson
Model 19 357 Combat Magnum
Same as Model 15 38 Combat Masterpiece except: 2½", 4", or 6" barrel; 357 magnum & 38 Special; round or square butt; add 2% for square butt target stocks & 6% for target sights
Estimated Value: $225.00 - $285.00

Smith & Wesson
Model 66 357 Combat Magnum
Same as Model 19 357 Combat Magnum except: satin finish stainless steel; add 12% for target accessories; 2% for target sights
Estimated Value: $250.00 - $315.00

Smith & Wesson Model 66

Smith & Wesson Model 60
Smith & Wesson
Model 36 Chiefs Special

Smith & Wesson
Model 17 K-22 Masterpiece
Same as Model 14 K-38 Masterpiece except: 22 short, long, long rifle caliber; 4", 6", or 8⅜" barrel; add $12.00 for 8⅜" barrel; add 9% for target trigger & hammer.
Estimated Value: $235.00 - $295.00

Smith & Wesson Model 18 22 Combat Masterpiece
Same as Model 17 K-22 Masterpiece except: 4" barrel; add 10% for target trigger & hammer
Estimated Value: $200.00 - $250.00

Smith & Wesson Model 36 Chiefs Special
Caliber: 38 Special
Action: Single & double; exposed hammer; solid frame
Cylinder: 5-shot swing out; simultaneous manual ejector; release on left side of frame
Barrel: 2" or 3"
Finish: Blued or nickel; round or square butt, checkered walnut grips; add $10.00 for nickel
Estimated Value: $210.00 - $260.00

Smith & Wesson Model 60 Chiefs Special Stainless
Same as Model 36 Chiefs special except: satin finish stainless steel construction; round butt grip; add 6% for 3" barrel
Estimated Value: $240.00 - $300.00

Smith & Wesson
Model 37 Airweight

Smith & Wesson
Model 37 Airweight Chiefs Special
Same as Model 36 Chiefs Special except: light alloy frame; add 4% for nickel finish
Estimated Value: $225.00 - $280.00

Smith & Wesson Model 40
Centennial Hammerless

Smith & Wesson
Model 40 Centennial Hammerless
Same as Model 36 Chiefs Special except: concealed hammer; frame extends over hammer area; 2" barrel; double action only; grip safety located on rear of grip
Estimated Value: $220.00 - $275.00

Smith & Wesson
Model 42 Centennial Airweight
Same as Model 40 Centennial except: light alloy frame
Estimated Value: $230.00 - $290.00

Smith & Wesson Model 42
Centennial Airweight

Smith & Wesson
Model 38 Bodyguard Airweight
Same as Model 36 Chiefs Special except: light alloy frame; shrouded hammer; 2" barrel only; add 3% for nickel finish
Estimated Value: $235.00 - $295.00

Smith & Wesson Model 38
Bodyguard Airweight

Smith & Wesson Model 49
Bodyguard

Smith & Wesson
Model 49 Bodyguard
Same as Model 38 Bodyguard Airweight except: steel frame
Estimated Value: $220.00 - $280.00

Smith & Wesson Model 649
Similar to the Model 49 Bodyguard except stainless steel
Estimated Value: $255.00 - $320.00

Smith & Wesson Model 57

Smith & Wesson Model 58

Smith & Wesson
Model 53 22 Jet Magnum
Caliber: 22 Rem. Jet center fire & 22 short, long, long rifle by using chamber inserts & repositioning floating firing pin in hammer; also could be fitted with 22 caliber extra cylinder; add $100.00 for extra cylinder
Action: Single & double; exposed hammer; solid frame
Cylinder: 6-shot swing out; simultaneous manual ejector; cylinder release on left side of frame
Barrel: 4", 6", or 8⅜"
Finish: Blued; checkered walnut target grips
Estimated Value: $440.00 - $550.00

Smith & Wesson
Model 29 44 Magnum
Caliber: 44 magnum & 44 Special
Action: Single & Double; exposed hammer; solid frame
Cylinder: 6-shot swing out; simultaneous manual ejector; release on left side of frame
Barrel: 4", 6", 8⅝", or 10⅝" ribbed; add 2% for 8⅜" barrel & 11% for 10⅝" barrel
Finish: Blued or nickel: checkered wood grips; add 2% for nickel finish; add $40.00 for presentation case
Estimated Value: $300.00 - $375.00

Smith & Wesson
Model 57 41 Magnum
Caliber: 41 magnum
Action: Single & double; exposed hammer; solid frame
Cylinder: 6-shot swing out; simultaneous manual ejector; release on left side of frame
Barrel: 4", 6", or 8⅜"
Finish: Blued or nickel; checkered walnut grips; add 4% for 8⅜" barrel
Estimated Value: $265.00 - $335.00

Smith & Wesson Model 58 M& P
Similar to Model 57 41 mag. except: 4" barrel only; fixed sights; no rib on barrel; add $10.00 for nickel
Estimated Value: $240.00 - $300.00

Smith & Wesson
Model 657 41 Magnum
Similar to the Model 57 41 Magnum except stainless steel; add 4% for 8⅜" barrel
Estimated Value: $280.00 - $355.00

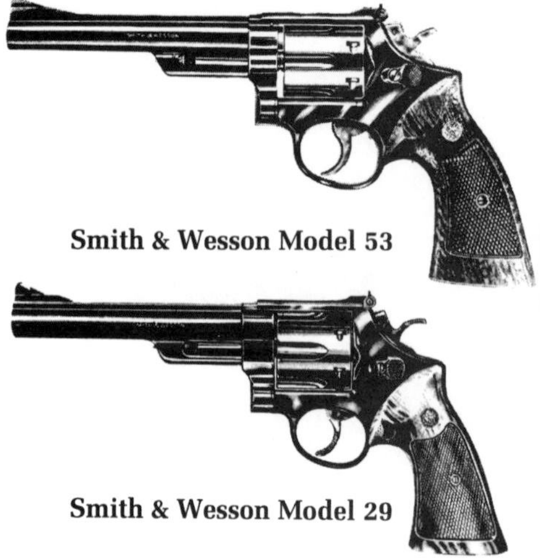
Smith & Wesson Model 53

Smith & Wesson Model 29

Smith & Wesson
Model 29 Classic 44 Magnum
Similar to the Model 29 44 Magnum except: 5", 6", or 8⅝" barrel; full lug barrel; interchangeable front sight; add 2% for 8⅝" barrel
Estimated Value: $325.00 - $405.00

Smith & Wesson Model 629

Smith & Wesson Model 629
Same as the Model 29 except: satin stainless steel; add 3% for 8⅜" barrel; add $40.00 for presentation case; 10⅝" barrel not available
Estimated Value: $320.00 - $400.00

Smith & Wesson Model 629 Classic
Similar to the Model 29 Classic 44 Magnum except: stainless steel construction; add 3% for 8⅜" barrel
Estimated Value: $340.00 - $425.00

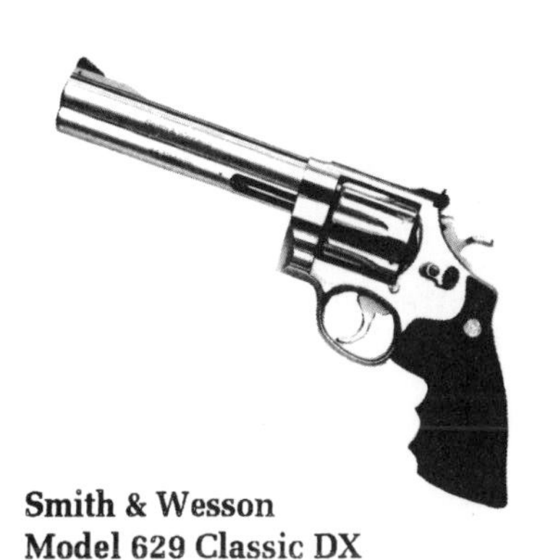

Smith & Wesson
Model 629 Classic DX

Smith & Wesson
Model 29 Classic DX
Similar to the Model 29 Classic except: combat grips; add 2% for 8⅝" barrel
Estimated Value: $425.00 - $535.00

Smith & Wesson
Model 629 Classic DX
Similar to the Model 29 Classic DX except: stainless steel construction; add 3% for 8⅝" barrel
Estimated Value: $450.00 - $565.00

Smith & Wesson Model 63
1977 22/32 Kit Gun
Caliber: 22 long rifle
Action: Single & double; exposed hammer
Cylinder: 6-shot swing out
Barrel: 4"
Finish: Stainless steel, satin finish; checkered walnut grips
Estimated Value: $250.00 - $315.00

Smith & Wesson Model 63

Smith & Wesson Model 581
Distinguished Service Magnum
Caliber: 357 magnum & 38 Special
Action: Single & double; exposed hammer; solid frame
Cylinder: 6-shot swing out; simultaneous manual ejector; release on left side of frame
Barrel: 4" or 6" heavy barrel with full-length ejector shroud
Finish: Blued or nickel; checkered walnut magna service grips; Smith & Wesson's new "L" frame revolver; slightly larger than the "K" frame
Estimated Value: $220.00 - $275.00

Smith & Wesson Model 681
Distinguished Service Magnum
Similar to the Model 581 except: satin stainless steel and 4" barrel
Estimated Value: $220.00 - $310.00

Smith & Wesson Model 686 Distinguished Combat Magnum

Smith & Wesson Model 625-2
Caliber: 45ACP
Action: Single & double; exposed hammer; solid frame
Cylinder: 6-shot swing out; simultaneous manual ejector
Barrel: 3", 4", or 5"; full-length ejector housing
Finish: Stainless steel; Pachmayr Gripper round butt grips
Estimated Value: $320.00 - $400.00

Smith & Wesson Model 586 Distinguished Combat Magnum

Smith & Wesson Model 586
Distinguished Combat Magnum
Caliber: 357 magnum & 38 Special
Action: Single & double; exposed hammer; solid frame
Cylinder: 6-shot swing out; simultaneous manual ejector; cylinder release on left side
Barrel: 4", 6", or 8⅜" heavy barrel with a full-length ejector shroud; add 5% for 8⅜" barrel
Finish: Blued or nickel; checkered Goncalo Alves target grips; add 3% for nickel finish; Smith & Wesson's new "L" frame revolver; slightly larger than the "K" frame; add 9% for adjustable front sight
Estimated Value: $250.00 - $315.00

Smith & Wesson Model 686
Distinguished Combat Magnum
Similar to the Model 586 except: satin stainless steel finish; add 2% for target grips; add 7% for adjustable front sight; add 6% for 8⅜" barrel; also available with 2½" barrel
Estimated Value: $260.00 - $330.00

Smith & Wesson Model 625-2

Smith & Wesson Model 547 Military & Police

Smith & Wesson
Model 547 Military & Police
Caliber: 9mm Parabellum
Action: Single & double; exposed hammer; solid frame
Cylinder: 6-shot swing out; simultaneous manual ejector; release on left side of frame
Barrel: 3" or 4" heavy barrel
Finish: Blued; checkered walnut round butt grips with 3" barrel & square butt with 4" barrrel; a 9mm revolver built on a "K" frame that features a unique new extraction system for positive extraction of the 9mm cartridge
Estimated Value: $210.00 - $260.00

Smith & Wesson
Model 36 Lady Smith
Caliber: 38 special
Action: Single & double action with exposed hammer; solid frame
Cylinder: 5-shot swing out; simultaneous manual ejector
Barrel: 2" or 3" heavy barrel
Finish: Blued; 2" barrel has smooth wood grips; 3" heavy barrel has smooth wood combat-style grips.
Estimated Value: $230.00 - $290.00

Smith & Wesson Model 60 Lady Smith

Smith & Wesson
Model 60 Lady Smith
Same as the Model 36 except all stainless steel
Estimated Value: $260.00 - $325.00

Smith & Wesson Model 16

Smith & Wesson Model 16
Caliber: 32 S&W or 32 magnum
Action: Single & double; exposed hammer; solid frame
Cylinder: 6-shot swing out; simultaneous manual ejector
Barrel: 4", 6", or 8⅜"; full-length ejector rod housing
Finish: Blued with square butt Goncalo Alves combat style grips; add 3% for 6" barrel; add 4% for 8⅜" barrel; add 7% for target trigger & target hammer
Estimated Value: $250.00 - $315.00

Smith & Wesson
Model 617 K-22 Masterpiece
Caliber: 22 short, long, long rifle
Action: Single & double action; exposed hammer; solid frame
Cylinder: 6-shot swing out; simultaneous manual ejector
Barrel: 4", 6", or 8³⁄₈"; full-length ejector housing; add 3% for 8³⁄₈" barrel
Finish: Stainless steel with square butt Goncalo Alves combat style grips; add 8% for target trigger & hammer
Estimated Value: $250.00 - $315.00

Smith & Wesson Model 648
Same as the Model 617 except: 6" barrel; 22 magnum caliber
Estimated Value: $250.00 - $315.00

Smith & Wesson Model 617

Smith & Wesson Model 651 Kit Gun

Smith & Wesson Model 650
Service Kit Gun
Caliber: 22 magnum
Action: Single & double action, exposed hammer
Cylinder: 6-shot swing out, simultaneous ejector
Barrel: 3" heavy barrel
Finish: Satin stainless steel; checkered walnut round butt grips
Estimated Value: $220.00 - $275.00

Smith & Wesson Model 651 Kit Gun
Caliber: 22 magnum
Action: Double & single, exposed hammer
Clynder: 6-shot swing out, simultaneous ejector
Barrel: 4"
Finish: Satin stainless steel; checkered walnut square butt grips
Estimated Value: $250.00 - $300.00

Smith & Wesson
Model 640 Centennial
Caliber: 38 Special
Action: Double action only; concealed hammer; solid frame
Cylinder: 5-shot swing out; simultaneous manual ejector
Barrel: 2" or 3"
Finish: Stainless steel with smooth Goncalo Alves round butt grips
Estimated Value: $250.00 - $315.00

Smith & Wesson
Model 650 Service Kit Gun

Taurus

Taurus Model 80, 82

Taurus Model 65
Caliber: 357 magnum or 38 Special
Action: Single or double action; exposed hammer
Cylinder: 6-shot swing out, simultaneous ejector
Barrel: 3" or 4" heavy barrel
Finish: Royal blue or satin nickel; checkered walnut grips; add 5% for satin nickel finish
Estimated Value: $150.00 - $185.00

Taurus Model 66
Similar to the Model 65 except: 3", 4", or 6" barrel; blued, satin nickel, or stainless steel; checkered walnut target grip on 6"; add 5% for satin nickel finish; add 27% for stainless steel
Estimated Value: $165.00 - $205.00

Taurus Model 669 and 689
Same as the Model 66 except: 4" or 6" barrel, full shroud under barrel; blued or stainless steel only; add 26% for stainless steel; 689 has ventilated rib (add 3%)
Estimated Value: $170.00 - $215.00

Taurus Model 80, 82
Caliber: 38 Special
Action: Single or double action; exposed hammer
Cylinder: 6-shot swing out; simultaneous ejector
Barrel: 3" or 4"; standard barrel (Model 80); heavy barrel (Model 82)
Finish: Blued or satin nickel; add 6.5% for satin nickel finish; checkered walnut grips
Estimated Value: $130.00 - $165.00

Taurus Model 83
Similar to the Model 82 except: 4" heavy barrel only; ramp front sight & micrometer adjustable rear sight; add 5% for satin nickel finish
Estimated Value: $135.00 - $170.00

Taurus Model 86 Target Master, 96 Target Scout
Caliber: 38 Special (86); 22 (96)
Action: Single or double; exposed hammer
Cylinder: 6-shot swing out; simultaneous ejector
Barrel: 6"
Finish: Blued; checkered walnut target grip
Estimated Value: $185.00 - $230.00

Taurus Model 86 Target Master, 96 Target Scout

Revolvers

Taurus Model 73
Caliber: 32 H&R magnum
Action: Single or double action; exposed hammer
Cylinder: 6-shot, swing out; simultaneous ejector
Barrel: 3" heavy barrel
Finish: Blued or satin nickel; add 10% for satin nickel finish
Estimated Value: $135.00 - $165.00

Taurus Model 76

Taurus Model 76
Similar to the Model 73 except: blued finish only; 6" barrel
Estimated Value:$185.00 - $230.00

Taurus Model 85

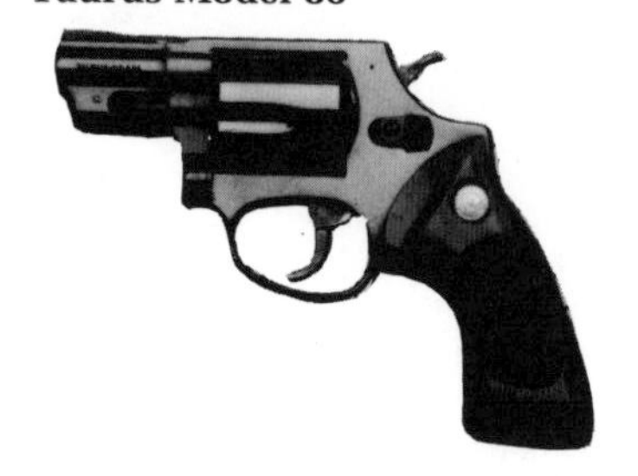

Taurus Model 85
Caliber: 38 Special
Action: Single or double action; exposed hammer
Cylinder: 5-shot swing out, simultaneous ejector
Barrel: 2" or 3" heavy barrel
Finish: Royal blue, satin nickel, or stainless steel; add 7% for satin nickel; add 25% for stainless steel
Estimated Value: $140.00 - $180.00

Taurus Model 85CH
Same as the Model 85 except: 2" barrel, spurless hammer; double action only; add 25% for stainless steel
Estimated Value: $140.00 - $175.00

Webley

Webley & Scott Mark III Government

Webley & Scott
Mark III Government Model
Caliber: 450, 455, or 476 Webley
Action: Single or double; exposed hammer; hinged frame; top break; simultaneous ejector
Cylinder: 6-shot
Barrel: 4", 6", or 7½"
Finish: Blued; hard rubber or wood grips
Estimated Value: $150.00 - $200.00

Webley & Scott Pocket Model Hammerless
Caliber: 32 S&W
Action: Double action; concealed hammer; hinged frame; top break; simultaneous ejector
Cylinder: 6-shot
Barrel: 3½"
Finish: Blued; hard rubber or wood grips
Estimated Value: $145.00 - $190.00

Webley & Scott Police & Civilian Pocket
Similar to Pocket Model Hammerless except: exposed hammer; double & single action
Estimated Value: $135.00 - $180.00

Webley & Scott Mark III Police

Webley & Scott Mark III Police
Caliber: 38 S&W
Action: Single or double; exposed hammer; hinged frame; top break simultaneous ejector
Cylinder: 6-shot
Barrel: 3", 4", or 5"
Finish: Blued; checkered hard rubber or walnut grips
Estimated Value: $150.00 - $190.00

Webley Mark IV

Webley Mark IV Police Model
Caliber: 38 S&W
Action: Single or double; exposed hammer; hinged frame; top break; simultaneous ejector
Cylinder: 6-shot
Barrel: 4", 5", or 6"
Finish: Blued; checkered walnut or plastic grips
Estimated Value: $140.00 - $185.00

Webley Mark IV War Model
Similar to Mark IV Police Model except: made during World War II; poorer finish & fitting
Estimated Value: $130.00 - $175.00

Webley Mark IV Pocket Model
Similar to Mark IV Police Model except: calibers 32 S&W, 32 S&W long, or 38 S&W; barrel length 3"
Estimated Value: $140.00 - $180.00

Webley Mark IV Pocket Model

Webley Mark IV Target Model
Similar to Mark IV Police Model except: caliber 22 short, long, or long rifle only; adjustable rear sight; 6" barrel
Estimated Value: $175.00 - $230.00

Webley Mark VI British Service

Webley Mark VI British Service
Caliber: 455 Webley
Action: Single or double; hinged frame; top break; simultaneous ejector
Cylinder: 6-shot
Barrel: 4", 6", or 7½"
Finish: Blued; checkered hard rubber or wood grips
Estimated Value: $170.00 - $220.00

Webley Police Mark VI Target
Similar to Mark VI British except: caliber 22 short, long, or long rifle; 6" barrel
Estimated Value: $180.00 - $225.00

Webley Police Mark VI Target

Section III

Semi-automatics

AMT

AMT On Duty DA
Caliber: 9mm, 40 S&W, 45ACP
Action: Semi-automatic; double action only with trigger disconnect thumb safety or decocker model
Magazine: 15-shot (9mm), 11-shot (40 S&W), 9-shot (45)
Barrel: 4½"
Finish: Anodized black matte; carbon fiber grips
Estimated Value: $315.00 - $395.00

AMT Lightning Pistol
Caliber: 22 long rifle
Action: Semi-automatic, concealed hammer
Magazine: 10-shot clip
Barrel: 5" bull, 6½" tapered or bull, 8½" tapered or bull, 10" tapered or bull, 12½" tapered; add 5% for 12½
Finish: Stainless steel; rubber wrap-around grips
Estimated Value: $180.00 - $225.00

AMT Combat Government

AMT Hardballer

AMT Combat Government
Caliber: 45 ACP
Action: Semi-automatic; exposed hammer; loaded chamber indicator; manual and grip safeties; adjustable target-type trigger
Magazine: 7-shot clip
Barrel: 5"
Finish: Checkered walnut grips; all stainless steel construction
Estimated Value: $345.00 - $430.00

AMT Hardballer
Same as the AMT Combat Government except; adjustable combat-type sights; serrated matte slide rib; grooved front and backstraps.
Estimated Value: $375.00 - $470.00

AMT Skipper
Same as the AMT Hardballer except 4" barrel
Estimated Value: $320.00 - $400.00

AMT Hardballer Long Slide
Same as the AMT Hardballer except: 7" barrel
Estimated Value: $390.00 - $490.00

AMT 380 Backup

AMT Backup
Caliber: 380 ACP, 22 long rifle
Action: Semi-automatic; concealed hammer; manual and grip safeties; also double action only model in 1992
Magazine: 5-shot clip in 380 ACP; 8-shot in 22LR
Barrel: 2½"
Finish: Smooth wood grips; all stainless steel construction; Lexon grips on later models
Estimated Value: $160.00 - $200.00

AMT Automag II
Caliber: 22 magnum
Action: Gas assisted, semi-automatic
Magazine: 9-shot clip
Barrel: 3⅜", 4½", or 6"
Finish: Grooved carbon-fiber grips; stainless steel construction
Estimated Value: $225.00 - $280.00

American

American 25 Automatic

American 25 Automatic
Caliber: 25 ACP; 250 magnum (after 1980)
Action: Semi-automatic; concealed hammer
Magazine: 8-shot clip; 7-shot in magnum
Barrel: 2"
Finish: Blue or stainless steel; smooth rosewood grips; finger extension on clip; add 20% for mag.
Estimated Value:
Blue: $95.00 - $125.00
Stainless: $115.00 - $150.00

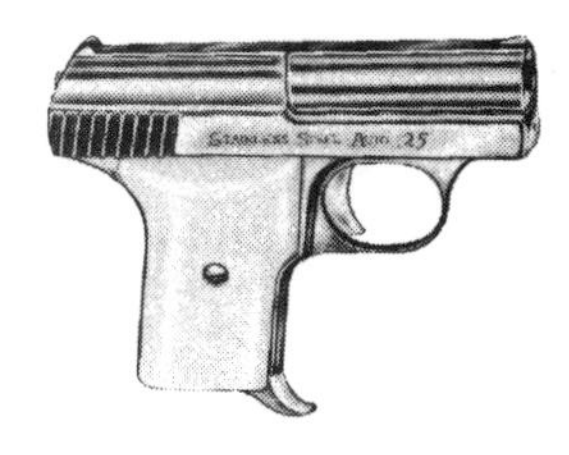

American Baby Model

American Baby Model
Similar to the 25 Automatic except slightly more compact, 6-shot clip
Estimated Value: $90.00 - $120.00

Astra

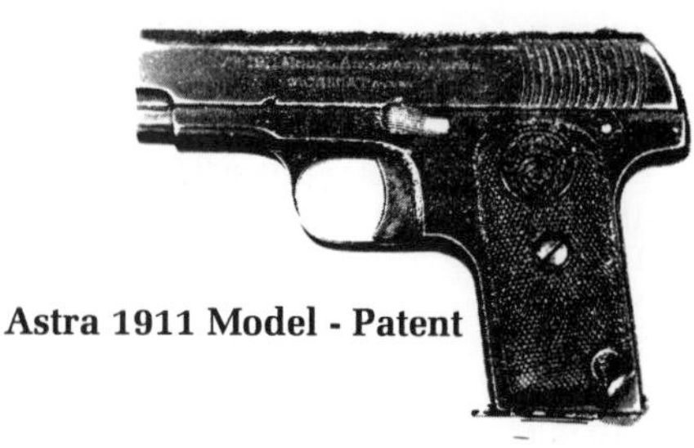
Astra 1911 Model - Patent

Astra 1911 Model - Patent
Caliber: 32 ACP (7.65mm)
Action: Semi-automatic, concealed hammer
Magazine: 7-shot clip
Barrel: 3¼"
Finish: Blued; checkered hard rubber grips
Estimated Value: $120.00 - $150.00

Astra 1915 Model - Patent
Caliber: 32 ACP (7.65mm)
Action: Semi-automatic, concealed hammer
Magazine: 9-shot clip
Barrel: 3¼"
Finish: Blued; checkered hard rubber grips
Estimated Value: $100.00 - $130.00

Astra 1915 Model - Patent

Astra 1916 Model - Patent
Caliber: 32 ACP (7.65mm)
Action: Semi-automatic, concealed hammer
Magazine: 9-shot clip
Barrel: 4"
Finish: Blued; checkered hard rubber or wood grips
Estimated Value: $110.00 - $135.00

Astra 1924 Hope

Astra 1924 Hope
Caliber: 25 ACP (6.35)
Action: Semi-automatic; concealed hammer
Magazine: 6-shot clip
Barrel: 2
Finish: Blued; checkered rubber grip
Estimated Value: $120.00 - $150.00

Astra 2000 Cub Pocket
Caliber: 22 short, 25 ACP (6.35mm)
Action: Semi-automatic; exposed hammer
Magazine: 6-shot clip
Barrel: 2⅛"
Finish: Blued; chrome and/or engraved, checkered grips
Estimated Value: $140.00 - $180.00

Astra Model 2000 Cub Pocket

Astra Camper Pocket
Same as Astra Cub (Model 2000) except: 22 caliber short only; 4" barrel which extends beyond front of slide
Estimated Value: $110.00 - $160.00

Astra Model 300
Caliber: 380 ACP (9mm Kurz)
Action: Semi-automatic; concealed hammer
Magazine: 7-shot clip
Barrel: 4¼"
Finish: Blued; checkered rubber grips
Estimated Value: $200.00 - $250.00

Astra Model 600

Astra Model 600
Caliber: 32 ACP (7.65mm), 9mm Luger
Action: Semi-automatic; concealed hammer
Magazine: 10-shot clip in 32 caliber; 8-shot clip in 9mm
Barrel: 5¼"
Finish: Blued; checkered rubber or wood grips
Estimated Value: $220.00 - $275.00

Astra Model 400
Caliber: 9mm Bayard long; 38 ACP, 9mm Steyr, 9mm Glisenti, 9mm Luger, 9mm Browning long cartridges can be used due to chamber design
Action: Semi-automatic; concealed hammer
Magazine: 9-shot clip
Barrel: 6"
Finish: Blued; checkered rubber grips
Estimated Value: $260.00 - $325.00

Astra Model 400

Semi-automatics

Astra Model 800 Condor
Caliber: 9mm Parabellum
Action: Semi-automatic; exposed hammer
Magazine: 8-shot clip
Barrel: 5¼"
Finish: Blued; checkered grips
Estimated Value: $255.00 - $320.00

Astra Model 200 Firecat

Astra Model 200 Firecat
Caliber: 25 ACP (6.35mm)
Action: Semi-automatic; concealed hammer; grip safety
Magazine: 6-shot clip
Barrel: 2¼"
Finish: Blued or chrome; plastic grips
Estimated Value: $140.00 - $175.00

Astra Model 3000

Astra Model 4000 Falcon

Astra Model 3000
Caliber: 22 long rifle, 32 ACP, 380ACP (9mm short)
Action: Semi-automatic; concealed hammer
Magazine: 10-shot clip in 22 caliber, 7-shot clip in 32 caliber; 6-shot clip in 380
Barrel: 4"
Finish: Blued; checkered grips
Estimated Value: $175.00 - $220.00

Astra Model A-80, A-90
Caliber: 9mm Parabellum, 38 Super, 45 ACP
Action: Double action; semi-automatic; exposed hammer
Magazine: 15-shot clip in 9mm and 38 calibers; 9-shot clip in 45 ACP
Barrel: 3¾"
Finish: Blued or chrome; checkered plastic grips
Estimated Value: $300.00 - $375.00

Astra Model 4000 Falcon
Caliber: 22 long rifle, 32 ACP (7.65mm), 380 ACP (9mm short)
Action: Semi-automatic; exposed hammer
Magazine: 10-shot clip in 22 caliber; 8-shot clip in 32 caliber; 7-shot clip in 380 caliber
Barrel: 4¼"
Finish: Blued; checkered grips
Estimated Value: $185.00 - $230.00

Astra Model 5000 Constable

Astra Model 5000 Constable
Caliber: 22 long rifle, 32 ACP (7.65mm), (32 discontinued), 380 ACP
Action: Double action; semi-automatic; exposed hammer with round spur
Magazine: 10-shot clip in 22 caliber long rifle, 8-shot clip in 32 ACP; 7-shot clip in 380 ACP
Barrel: 3½"; 6" on Sport model
Finish: Blued or chrome; grooved grips; checkered on late model; plastic or wood grips
Estimated Value: $210.00 - $260.00

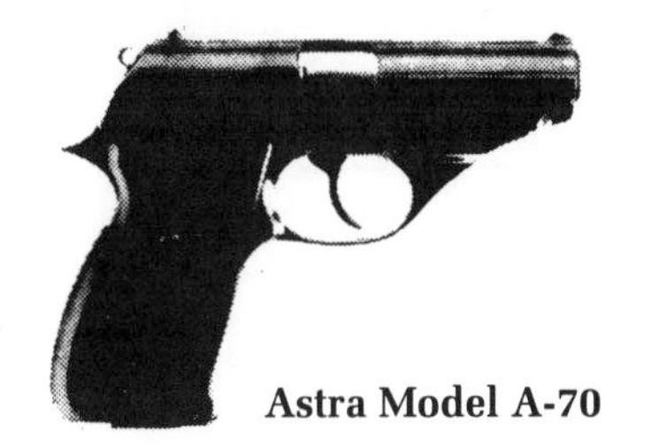

Astra Model A-70

Astra Model A-70
Caliber: 9mm Parabellum, 40 S&W
Action: Double action; semi-automatic; exposed hammer
Magazine: 8-shot clip
Barrel: 3½"
Finish: Blued or chrome; checkered plastic grips
Estimated Value: $250.00 - $310.00

Auto Mag

Auto Mag

Auto Mag
Caliber: 357 auto magnum or 44 auto magnum custom loaded or hand loaded cartridges (no commerical ammo available)
Action: Semi-automatic; exposed hammer; adjustable trigger
Magazine: 7-shot clip
Barrel: 6½" ventilated rib (44 auto magnum); 6½" or 8½" (357 auto magnum); no rib on 8½" barrel
Finish: Stainless steel; black polyurethane grips
Estimated Value: $1,200.00 - $2,400.00

Bauer

Bauer Stainless

Bauer Stainless
Caliber: 25 ACP
Action: Semi-automatic; concealed hammer
Magazine: 6-shot clip
Barrel: 2⅛"
Finish: Heat treated stainless steel; plastic grips
Estimated Value: $100.00 - $125.00

Bayard

Bayard Model 1908

Bayard Model 1908
Caliber: 25 ACP (6.35mm), 32 ACP (7.65mm), 380 ACP (9mm short)
Action: Semi-automatic; concealed hammer
Magazine: 6-shot clip
Barrel: 2¼"
Finish: Blued; checkered grips
Estimated Value: $130.00 - $175.00

Bayard Model 1923

Bayard Model 1923 (32, 380)
Caliber: 32 ACP (7.65mm), 380 ACP (9mm short)
Action: Semi-automatic; concealed hammer
Magazine: 6-shot clip
Barrel: 3⅜"
Finish: Blued; checkered grips
Estimated Value: $165.00 - $225.00

Bayard Model 1923 (25 ACP)
Caliber: 25 ACP
Action: Semi-automatic; concealed hammer
Magazine: 6-shot clip
Barrel: 2⅛"
Finish: Blued; checkered grips
Length Overall: 4⅓"
Estimated Value: $145.00 - $190.00

Bayard Model 1930

Bayard Model 1930
Caliber: 25 ACP (6.35mm)
Action: Semi-automatic; concealed hammer
Magazine: 6-shot clip
Barrel: 2"
Finish: Blued; checkered grips
Estimated Value: $160.00 - $200.00

Beretta

Beretta Model 1915
Caliber: 32 ACP (7.65mm)
Action: Semi-automatic; concealed hammer
Magazine: 8-shot clip
Barrel: 3¼"
Finish: Blued; wood or metal grips
Estimated Value: $220.00 - $275.00

Beretta Model 1915

Beretta Model 1919 "Bantam"

Beretta Model 1919 Bantam
Caliber: 25 ACP (6.35mm)
Action: Semi-automatic; concealed hammer
Magazine: 7-shot clip
Barrel: 2½"
Finish: Blued; wood grips
Estimated Value: $160.00 - $200.00

Beretta Model 1923

Beretta Model 1923
Caliber: 9mm Luger
Action: Semi-automatic; exposed hammer
Magazine: 9-shot clip
Barrel: 4"
Finish: Blued; wood grips
Estimated Value: $265.00 - $330.00

Semi-automatics

Beretta Model 1931
Caliber: 32 ACP (7.65mm)
Action: Semi-automatic; concealed hammer
Magazine: 7-shot clip
Barrel: 3⁵⁄₁₆"
Finish: Blued; wood grips
Estimated Value: $220.00 - $275.00

Beretta Model 934 (1934) 380 & 935 (1935) 32
Caliber: 32 ACP (7.65mm), 380 ACP (9mm short)
Action: Semi-automatic; exposed hammer
Magazine: 8-shot clip in 32; 7-shot clip in 380
Barrel: 3½"
Finish: Blued; plastic grips
Estimated Value: $230.00 - $290.00

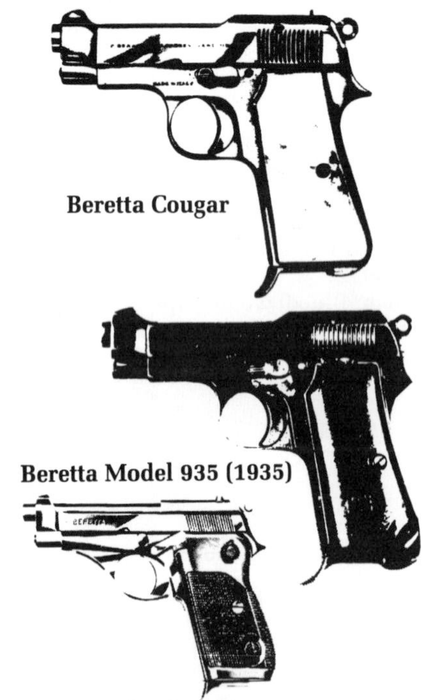

Beretta Cougar

Beretta Model 935 (1935)

Beretta Model 70 Puma

Beretta Model 1931

Beretta Model 934 (1934)

Beretta Cougar
Caliber: 380 ACP (9mm short)
Action: Semi-automatic; exposed hammer
Magazine: 7-shot clip
Barrel: 3½"
Finish: Blued or chrome; plastic grips
Estimated Value: $220.00 - $275.00

Beretta Model 948 Plinker
Caliber: 22 long rifle
Action: Semi-automatic; exposed hammer
Magazine: 7-shot clip
Barrel: 3½", 6"
Finish: Blued; plastic grips
Estimated Value: $130.00 - $165.00

Beretta Model 70 Puma
Caliber: 32 ACP (7.65mm); 380 ACP
Action: Semi-automatic; exposed hammer
Magazine: 7-shot clip
Barrel: 3½"
Finish: Blued; plastic wrap-around grip
Estimated Value: $175.00 - $220.00

Beretta Model 70S

Beretta Model 70S
Caliber: 380 ACP (9mm short); 22 long rifle
Action: Semi-automatic; exposed hammer
Magazine: 7-shot clip in 380; 8-shot clip in 22
Barrel: 3½"
Finish: Blued; 2-piece wrap-around plastic grip
Estimated Value: $175.00 - $225.00

Beretta Model 70T

Beretta Model 70T
Caliber: 32 ACP (7.65mm)
Action: Semi-automatic; exposed hammer
Magazine: 9-shot clip
Barrel: 6"
Finish: Blued; plastic wrap-around grip
Estimated Value: $180.00 - $230.00

Beretta Model 101
Same as Model 70T except: 22 caliber long rifle; 10-shot clip.
Estimated Value: $170.00 - $210.00

Beretta Models 71 & 72 Jaguar
Caliber: 22 long rifle
Action: Semi-automatic; exposed hammer
Magazine: 7-shot clip
Barrel: 3½" (Model 71) and 6" (Model 72)
Finish: Blued; wrap-around plastic grip
Estimated Value: $180.00 - $225.00

Beretta Model 71 & 72 Jaguar

Beretta Model 949 Olympic, 949C
Caliber: 22 short, 22 long rifle
Action: Semi-automatic; exposed hammer
Magazine: 5-shot clip
Barrel: 8¾" with compensator muzzle brake
Finish: Blued; checkered walnut grips with thumb rest
Estimated Value: $390.00 - $490.00

Semi-automatics

Beretta Model 951 (1951)

Beretta Model 951 (1951)
Caliber: 9mm Parabellum (Luger)
Action: Semi-automatic; exposed hammer
Magazine: 8-shot clip
Barrel: 4½"
Finish: Blued; plastic wrap-around grip
Estimated Value: $270.00 - $335.00

Beretta Minx M2, Model 950 B, 950 BS
Caliber: 22 short, 25 ACP
Action: Semi-automatic; exposed hammer
Magazine: 6-shot clip
Barrel: 2½"
Finish: Blued or nickel; plastic grips; wood grips
Estimated Value: $100.00 - $135.00

Beretta Minx M2

Beretta Minx M-4, Model 950C, 950 BS4
Same as Minx M-2, except: 4" barrel
Estimated Value: $110.00 - $150.00

Beretta Jetfire Model 950B
Same as Minx M-2, except: 25 ACP (6.35mm)
Estimated Value: $100.00 - $145.00

Beretta Minx M-4 Model 950C

Beretta Model DA 380

Beretta Model DA 380
Caliber: 380 ACP (9mm short)
Action: Double action; semi-automatic; exposed round spur hammer
Magazine: 13-shot staggered clip
Barrel: 3¾"
Finish: Blued; smooth walnut grips
Estimated Value: $225.00 - $300.00

Beretta Model 76 Target
Caliber: 22 long rifle
Action: Semi-automatic; exposed hammer
Magazine: 10-shot clip
Barrel: 6"
Finish: Blued; 2-piece wrap around plastic or wood grip
Estimated Value: $230.00 - $300.00

Beretta Model 90
Caliber: 32 ACP (7.65mm short)
Action: Semi-automatic; straight blowback; double action; exposed hammer
Magazine: 8-shot clip
Barrel: 3½"
Finish: Blued; contoured plastic grips
Estimated Value: $220.00 - $290.00

Beretta Model 92, 92S
Caliber: 9mm Parabellum
Action: Semi-automatic; double and single action; loaded chamber indicator
Magazine: 15-shot staggered clip
Barrel: 5"
Finish: Blued; plastic or smooth wood grips
Estimated Value: $300.00 - $410.00

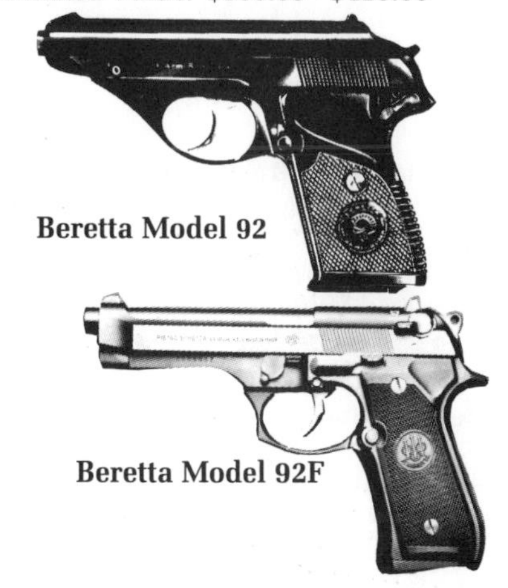

Beretta Model 92

Beretta Model 92F

Beretta Model 76

Beretta Model 90

Beretta Model 92SB
Caliber: 9mm Parabellum
Action: Semi-automatic; straight blowback; double action; exposed hammer
Magazine: 15-shot staggered clip
Barrel: 5"
Finish: Blued; walnut or checkered plastic grips
Estimated Value: $340.00 - $450.00

Beretta Model 92SB Compact
Similar to the Model 92SB except 4¼" barrel; 13-shot clip
Estimated Value: $375.00 - $465.00

Beretta Model 92F & 92FS (after 1991)
Caliber: 9mm Parabellum
Action: Double action semi-automatic, locked breech, delayed blowback, exposed hammer, manual ambidextrous safety; open top slide; adopted as side arm of the U.S. Military in mid 1980
Magazine: 15-shot staggered clip
Barrel: 5"
Finish: Combat-style alloy frame and steel matte finish slide or stainless steel slide; smooth or checkered plastic or wood grips; add 20% for S.S slide
Estimated Value: $375.00 - $470.00

Semi-automatics

Beretta Model 92G and 96G
Same as the Model 92FS except: hammer drop lever does not function as a traditional safety. When the lever is released after dropping the hammer, it returns to firing position. It can be fired (double action mode for first shot) by pulling the trigger. 96G is 40 S&W caliber with 10-shot clip; add 2% for Model 96G
Estimated V`alue: $375.00 - $470.00

Beretta Model 92F and 92FS Compact
Similar to the Model 92F with a 4¼" barrel, 13-shot clip
Estimated Value: $375.00 - $470.00

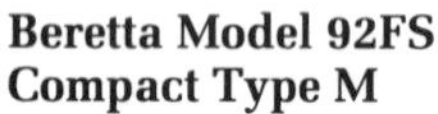

Beretta Model 92FS Compact Type M
Same as the Model 92FS Compact except: narrower grip, holding a single line 8-shot clip
Estimated Value: $375.00 - $470.00

Beretta Model 96 and 96 Compact
Same as the Model 92FS except: 40 S&W caliber with 10-shot clip; the 96 Compact is the same as Model 92FS Compact except 40 S&W caliber with 9-shot magazine
Estimated Value: $385.00 - $480.00

Beretta Model 92D/96G

Beretta Model 92F Compact

Beretta Model 92DS and 96DS
Same as the Model 92FS except: double action only; bobbed hammer; hammer returns to the down position after each slide cycle; also has safety lever; 96DS is 40 S&W caliber with 10-shot clip.
Estimated Value: $375.00 - $470.00

Beretta Model 92D and 96D
Same as the Model 92DS and 96DS except: the safety lever has been eliminated
Estimated Value: $350.00 - $440.00

Beretta Model 92FS Centurian
Same as the Model 92FS except: 4¼" barrel (as the 92FS Compact) but has the 15-shot clip (as the 92FS).
Estimated Value: $375.00 - $470.00

Beretta Model 96 Centurian
Same as the Model 92FS Centurian except: 40 S&W caliber with 10-shot clip
Estimated Value: $385.00 - $480.00

Beretta Model 20

Beretta Model 20
Caliber: 25 ACP
Action: Straight blowback, recoil ejection, double action semi-automatic
Magazine: 8-shot clip
Barrel: 2½" tip-up
Finish: Blued; alloy frame; plastic or walnut grips
Estimated Value: $120.00 - $175.00

Beretta Model 21
Caliber: 22 long rifle, 25 ACP
Action: Straight blowback, double action semi-automatic
Magazine: 7-shot clip (22 caliber); 8-shot clip (25ACP)
Barrel: 2½" tip up
Finish: Blued or nickel, alloy frame; wood grips
Estimated Value: $140.00 - $175.00

Beretta Model 81
Caliber: 32 ACP
Action: Semi-automatic; double & single action
Magazine: 12-shot clip
Barrel: 3¾"
Finish: Blued or nickel; plastic or smooth wood grips
Estimated Value: $265.00 - $335.00

Beretta Model 21

Beretta Model 84
Similar to the Model 81 in 380 caliber (9mm short); 13-shot clip; add 10% for nickel finish
Estimated Value: $310.00 - $390.00

Beretta Model 82
Caliber: 32 ACP (7.65mm)
Action: Semi-automatic; straight blowback; double action; exposed hammer
Magazine: 9-shot clip
Barrel: 3¾"
Finish: Blued or nickel, walnut grips; add 10% for nickel finish
Estimated Value: $270.00 - $340.00

Beretta Model 81

Beretta Model 85
Similar to the Model 82 except 380 caliber (9mm short) & 8-shot clip; add 10% for nickel
Estimated Value: $290.00 - $360.00

Beretta Model 86
Similar to the Model 85 with tip-up barrel for loading without working the slide; wood grips
Estimated Value: $330.00 - $415.00

Beretta Model 86

Beretta Model 87
Similar to the Model 85 but chambered for 22 long rifle, 7 shot; add 4% for 6" barrel & counter-weight.
Estimated Value: $295.00 - $365.00

Beretta Model 89
Caliber: 22 long rifle
Action: Single action, semi-automatic
Magazine: 8-shot clip
Barrel: 6"
Finish: Blued; walnut grips with thumb rest
Estimated Value: $440.00 - $550.00

Browning

Browning 25 Pocket
Caliber: 25 ACP (6.35mm)
Action: Semi-automatic; concealed hammer
Magazine: 6-shot clip
Barrel: 2⅛"
Finish: Blued; hard rubber grips; nickel plated, light-weight, plastic pearl grips; Renaissance engraved nickel, Nacolac pearl grips. Estimated Value is for blued model; add 10% for nickel plated model
Estimated Value: $190.00 - $240.00

Browning Model 1910

Browning Model 1910
Caliber: 380 ACP (9mm short), 32 ACP
Action: Semi-automatic; concealed hammer
Magazine: 6-shot clip
Barrel: 3½"
Finish: Blued; hard rubber grips; Renaissance engraved nickel, has Nacolac pearl grips. Estimated Value is for the blued model.
Estimated Value: $240.00 - $300.00

Browning Hi Power

Browning Challenger

Browning 9MM, Hi Power
Caliber: 9mm Parabellum
Action: Semi-automatic; exposed hammer; single action
Magazine: 13-shot clip
Barrel: 4⅝"
Finish: Blued; checkered walnut or molded Polymide grips; Renaissance engraved nickel, Nacolac pearl grips. Estimated Value is for blued model.
Estimated Value: $305.00 - $380.00

Browning Hi Power Mark III
Similar to the Hi Power with a nonglare matte blued finish, low profile sights, and two-piece molded grips with thumb rest
Estimated Value: $280.00 - $350.00

Browning Hi Power Practical
Similar to the Hi Power with contrasting blued slide and silver-chromed frame, wrap-around Pachmayr grips, round serrated hammer, and removable front sight
Estimated Value: $330.00 - $415.00

Browning Challenger
Caliber: 22 long rifle
Action: Semi-automatic; concealed hammer
Magazine: 10-shot clip
Barrel: 4½" or 6¾"
Finish: Blued; checkered walnut grips; Gold model (gold inlaid) finely figured walnut grips; Renaissance nickel engraved, finely figured walnut grips. Estimated Value is for blued model.
Estimated Value: $275.00 - $340.00

Browning Challenger II

Browning Challenger II
Similar to the Challenger except 6¾" barrel only; Impregnated wood grips
Estimated Value: $150.00 - $200.00

Semi-automatics

Browning Challenger III
Caliber: 22 long rifle
Action: Semi-automatic; concealed hammer
Magazine: 10-shot clip
Barrel: 5½" bull barrel
Finish: Blued; smooth impregnated hardwood grips
Estimated Value: $160.00 - $200.00

Browning Challenger III

Browning Challenger III Sporter
Similar to the Challenger III with 6¾" round barrel
Estimated Value: $150.00 - $190.00

Browning Nomad

Browning Nomad
Caliber: 22 long rifle
Action: Semi-automatic; concealed hammer
Magazine: 10-shot clip
Barrel: 4½" or 6¾"
Finish: Blued; plastic grips
Estimated Value: $190.00 - $250.00

Browning Model BDM
Caliber: 9mm Luger
Action: Semi-automatic; short recoil operated; double action with selector switch for double action only
Magazine: 15-shot clip
Barrel: 4¾"
Finish: Black matte; molded wrap-around grips
Estimated Value: $310.00 - $385.00

Browning Model BDA
Caliber: 45 ACP, 9mm, 38 Super ACP
Action: Semi-automatic; exposed hammer; built-in safety block; double and single action
Magazine: 7-shot clip in 45 ACP; 9-shot clip in 9mm and 38 Super
Barrel: 4½"
Finish: Blued; black checkered plastic grips
Estimated Value: $280.00 - $350.00

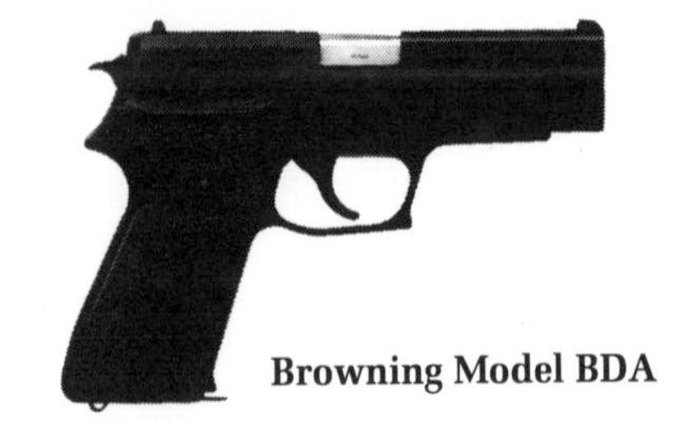

Browning Model BDA

Browning Buck Mark 22

Browning Buck Mark 22
Caliber: 22 long rifle
Action: Semi-automatic; blowback; concealed hammer
Magazine: 10-shot clip
Barrel: 5½" bull barrel with non-glare top
Finish: Blued; matte except for lustre barrel sides; checkered black molded composite grips, deer head medallion; brass-plated trigger; laminated wood grips (Buck Mark Plus); nickel finish available after 1991; add 12% for nickel finish and 15% for micro Buck mark plus
Estimated Value: $135.00 - $170.00

Browning Model BDA 380

Browning Model BDA 380
Caliber: 380 ACP
Action: Semi-automatic; exposed hammer; double and single action
Magazine: 12-shot staggered row clip
Barrel: 3¾"
Finish: Blued; smooth walnut grips, bronze medallion; nickel finish available after 1981; add 6% for nickel finish
Estimated Value: $340.00 - $425.00

Browning Medalist
Caliber: 22 long rifle
Action: Semi-automatic; concealed hammer
Magazine: 10-shot clip
Barrel: 6¾", ventilated rib
Finish: Blued; checkered walnut grips with thumb rest; Gold model (gold inlaid) and Nickel engraved Renaissance Model; finely figured and carved walnut grips with thumb rest. Estimated Value is for blued model.
Estimated Value: $460.00 - $575.00

Browning Micro Buck Mark
Similar to the Buck Mark with 4" barrel; add 12% for nickel finish and 15% for Micro Buck Mark Plus
Estimated Value: $135.00 - $170.00

Browning Buck Mark Silhouette
A silhouette-style pistol based on the Buck Mark design; 9⅞" bull barrel; walnut grips; fluted walnut forearm
Estimated Value: $230.00 - $285.00

Browning Buck Mark Varmint
A varmint-style pistol based on the Buck Mark design; 9⅞" bull barrel, walnut grips and walnut forearm
Estimated Value: $200.00 - $250.00

Browning Buck Mark 5.5
Similar to the Buck Mark with heavy round barrel with a unique top-ribbed design; add 7% for Gold Target model
Estimated Value: $215.00 - $270.00

Semi-automatics

Browning International Medalist

Browning International Medalist
Caliber: 22 long rifle
Action: Semi-automatic; hammerless
Magazine: 10-shot clip
Barrel: 5 15/16" heavy, counter weight
Finish: Blued; wide walnut grips, adjustable hand stop
Estimated Value: $450.00 - $565.00

Browning, FN

FN Browning Model 1900

FN Browning Model 1900
Caliber: 32 ACP (7.65mm)
Action: Semi-automatic; concealed hammer
Magazine: 7-shot clip
Barrel: 4"
Finish: Blued, hard rubber grips with FN trademark
Estimated Value: $225.00 - $300.00

FN Browning Model 1903 Military

FN Browning Model 1903 Military
Caliber: 9mm Browning long
Action: Semi-automatic; concealed hammer
Magazine: 7-shot clip
Barrel: 5"
Finish: Blued, hard rubber grips with FN trademark
Estimated Value: $220.00 - $290.00

FN Browning 6.35mm Pocket

FN Browning 6.35 mm Vest Pocket
Caliber: 25 ACP (6.35mm)
Action: Semi-automatic; concealed hammer; grip safety
Magazine: 6-shot clip
Barrel: 2"
Finish: Blued; hard rubber grips with FN trademark
Estimated Value: $250.00 - $335.00

FN Browning Model 1910

FN Browning Model 1910
Caliber: 32 ACP (7.65mm), 380 ACP (9mm short)
Action: Semi-automatic; concealed hammer
Magazine: 7-shot clip in 32 ACP, 6-short clip in 380
Barrel: 3½"
Finish: Blued, hard rubber grips with FN trademark
Estimated Value: $200.00 - $260.00

FN Browning Model 1922 Military and Police
Caliber: 32 ACP (7.65mm), 380 ACP (9mm short)
Action: Semi-automatic; concealed hammer
Magazine: 9-shot clip in 32; 8-shot clip in 380
Barrel: 4½"
Finish: Blued, hard rubber grips with FN trademark
Estimated Value: $170.00 - $225.00

FN Browning Model 1922 Military and Police

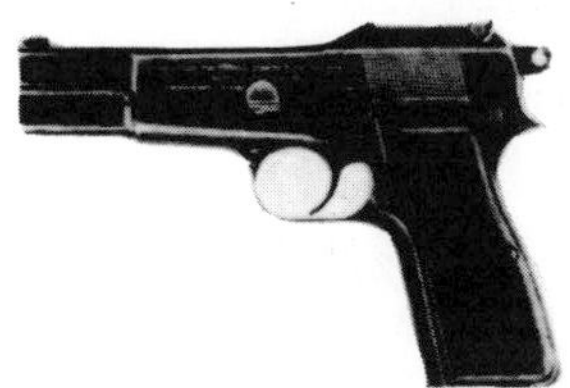

FN Browning Model 1935 Hi Power

FN Browning Model 1935 Hi Power
Caliber: 9mm Parabellum
Action: Semi-automatic; exposed hammer
Magazine: 13-shot staggered line clip
Barrel: 4⅝"
Finish: Blued or parkerized; checkered walnut or plastic grips
Estimated Value:
FN: $340.00 - $450.00
German: $265.00 - $350.00
Canadian: $300.00 - $390.00

FN Browning Baby

FN Baby Browning
Caliber: 25 ACP (6.35mm)
Action: Semi-automatic; concealed hammer
Magazine: 6-shot clip
Barrel: 2⅛"
Finish: Blued, hard rubber grips with FN trademark
Estimated Value: $275.00 - $360.00

CZ

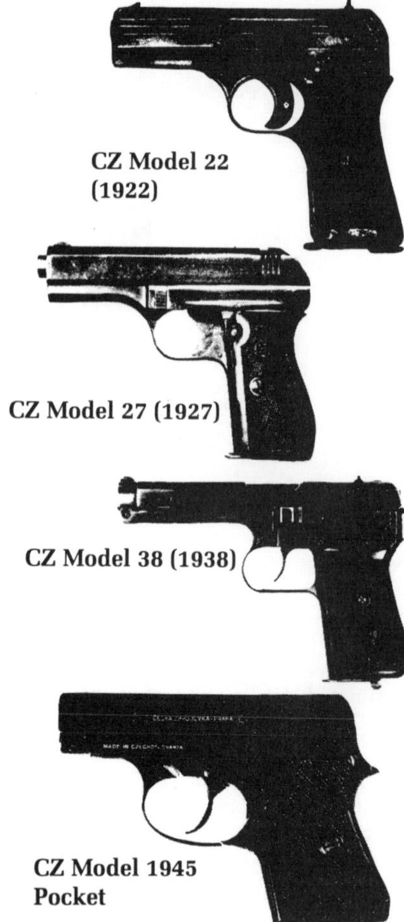
CZ Model 22 (1922)

CZ Model 27 (1927)

CZ Model 38 (1938)

CZ Model 1945 Pocket

CZ Model 22 (1922)
Caliber: 380 ACP (9mm short), 25 ACP
Action: Semi-automatic; exposed hammer with shielding on both sides
Magazine: 8-shot clip
Barrel: 3½"
Finish: Blued
Estimated Value: $145.00 - $190.00

CZ Model 1936 Pocket
Caliber: 25 ACP (6.5mm)
Action: Double action semi-automatic; slide does not cock hammer (hammer is cocked and released by the trigger); shielded exposed hammer
Magazine: 8-shot clip
Barrel: 2½"
Finish: Blued; plastic grips
Estimated Value: $140.00 - $180.00

CZ Model 1927 Pocket
Caliber: 32 ACP (7.65mm)
Action: Semi-automatic; exposed hammer with shielding on both sides
Magazine: 8-shot clip
Barrel: 4"
Finish: Blued; plastic grips
Estimated Value: $145.00 - $195.00

CZ Model 1945 Pocket
Same as CZ Model 1936 except for minor modifications. U.S. importation discontinued in 1968.
Estimated Value: $145.00 - $190.00

CZ Model 38 (1938)
Caliber: 380 ACP (9mm short)
Action: Double action; semi-automatic
Magazine: 9-shot clip
Barrel: 3¾"
Finish: Blued; plastic grips
Estimated Value: $175.00 - $220.00

CZ "Duo" Pocket
Caliber: 25 ACP (6.35mm)
Action: Semi-automatic; concealed hammer
Magazine: 6-shot clip
Barrel: 2⅛"
Finish: Blued; plastic grips
Estimated Value: $140.00 - $180.00

CZ Model 50 (1950)

CZ Model 50 (1950)
Caliber: 32 ACP (7.65mm)
Action: Semi-automatic; exposed hammer; double action
Magazine: 8-shot clip
Barrel: 3$\frac{1}{8}$"
Finish: Blued; plastic grips
Estimated Value: $160.00 - $210.00

CZ Model 70
Caliber: 7.65mm (32)
Action: Semi-automatic; exposed hammer; double action
Magazine: 8-shot clip
Barrel: 3$\frac{1}{8}$"
Finish: Blued; checkered plastic grips
Estimated Value: $170.00 - $225.00

CZ Model 75
Caliber: 9mm Parabellum
Action: Semi-automatic; selective double action; exposed hammer
Magazine: 15-shot clip
Barrel: 4$\frac{1}{2}$"
Finish: Blued; checkered plastic grips
Estimated Value: $310.00 - $400.00

Charter Arms

Charter Arms Explorer II

Charter Arms Explorer II
Caliber: 22 long rifle
Action: Semi-automatic
Magazine: 8-shot clip
Barrel: 6" or 10" interchangeable
Finish: Black, semi-gloss textured enamel; simulated walnut grips; extra clip storage in grip; also available in silvertone
Estimated Value: $70.00 - $90.00

Charter Arms Model 79K
Caliber: 380 Auto, 32 Auto
Action: Semi-automatic; double action; exposed hammer
Magazine: 7-shot clip
Barrel: 3½"
Finish: Stainless steel; checkered walnut grips
Estimated Value: $220.00 - $295.00

Charter Arms Model 79K

Charter Arms Model 40
Similar to the Model 79K except in 22 long rifle; 8-shot clip
Estimated Value: $180.00 - $240.00

Colt

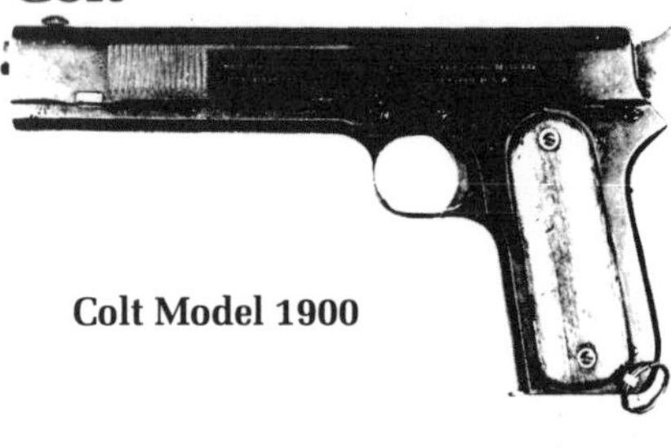
Colt Model 1900

Colt Model 1900
Caliber: 38 ACP
Action: Semi-automatic; exposed spur hammer; press down rear sight to block hammer (safety); no slide lock
Magazine: 7-shot clip
Barrel: 6"
Finish: Blued; plain walnut grips
Estimated Value: $640.00 - $800.00

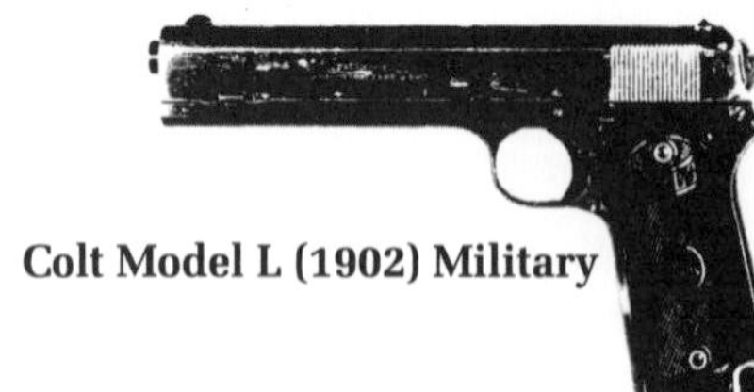
Colt Model L (1902) Military

Colt Model L (1902)
Similar to Colt Model 1900 except: no safety; rounded hammer spur; hard rubber grips
Estimated Value: $560.00 - $700.00

Colt Model L (1903) Pocket

Colt Model L (1902) Military
Same as Colt Model L (1902) except: longer grips (more square at bottom) with lanyard ring; 8-shot magazine; rounded or spur type hammer
Estimated Value: $640.00 - $800.00

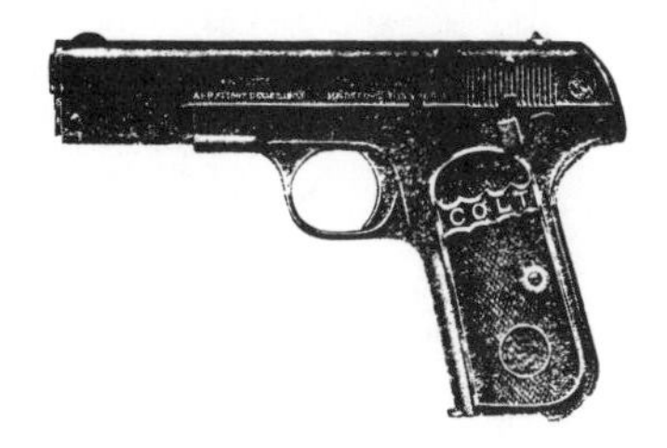

Colt Model M (32) 1st Issue Pocket

Colt Model L (1903) Pocket
Caliber: 38 ACP
Action: Semi-automatic; exposed hammer
Magazine: 7-shot clip
Barrel: 4½"
Finish: Blued; checkered hard rubber grips; rounded or spur type hammer
Estimated Value: $320.00 - $400.00

Colt Model M (32) 2nd Issue Pocket

Colt Model M (32) 1st Issue Pocket
Caliber: 32 ACP (7.65 mm short)
Action: Semi-automatic; concealed hammer; slide lock safety and grip safety; barrel lock bushing at muzzle
Magazine: 8-shot clip
Barrel: 3¾"
Finish: Blued or nickel; hard rubber or checkered walnut grips
Estimated Value: $320.00 - $400.00

Colt Model M (32) 2nd Issue Pocket
Similar to 1st Issue Model M (32) except: no barrel lock bushing ; other minor modifications; add $200.00 for Military Model
Estimated Value: $280.00 - $350.00

Colt Model M (32) 3rd Issue Pocket
Similar to 2nd Issue Model M (32) except: safety disconnector, which prevents cartridge in chamber from being fired if magazine is removed
Estimated Value: $300.00 - $375.00

Colt Model M (32) 3rd Issue Pocket

Colt Model M (380) 1st Issue Pocket

Colt Model M (380) 1st Issue Pocket
Caliber: 380 ACP (9 mm short)
Action: Semi-automatic; concealed hammer; slide lock safety and grip safety; barrel lock bushing at muzzle
Magazine: 7-shot clip
Barrel: 3¾"
Finish: Blued or nickel; hard rubber or checkered walnut grips.
Estimated Value: $325.00 - $410.00

Semi-automatics

Colt Model M (380) 2nd Issue Pocket
Similar to 1st Issue Model M (380) except: without barrel lock bushing and other minor changes; add $200.00 for Military Model.
Estimated Value: $285.00 - $360.00

Colt Model M (380) 2nd Issue Pocket

Colt Model M (380) 3rd Issue Pocket
Similar to 2nd Issue Model M (32) except: has safety disconnector, which prevents cartridge in chamber from being fired if magazine is removed
Estimated Value: $300.00 - $375.00

Colt Model 1905 Military
Caliber: 45 ACP
Action: Semi-automatic; exposed rounded or spur hammer; slide lock safety; some models had experimental short grip safeties
Magazine: 7-shot clip
Barrel: 5"
Finish: Blued; checkered walnut grips
Estimated Value: $800.00 - $1,000.00

Colt Model 1905 Military

Colt Model N Pocket

Colt Model N Pocket
Caliber: 25 ACP
Action: Semi-automatic; concealed hammer; thumb safety and grip safety
Magazine: 6-shot clip
Barrel: 2"
Finish: Blued or nickel; hard rubber or checkered walnut grips; add $200.00 for military model
Estimated Value: $245.00 - $325.00

Colt Junior Pocket Model 0-6
Caliber: 22 short, 25 ACP
Action: Semi-automatic; exposed round spur hammer
Magazine: 6-shot clip
Barrel: 2⅛"
Finish: Blued; checkered walnut grips
Estimated Value: $160.00 - $200.00

Colt Junior Pocket Model 0-6

Colt Government Model 1911

Colt Government Model 1911
Caliber: 45 ACP
Action: Semi-automatic; exposed spur hammer; thumb safety and grip safety
Magazine: 7-shot clip
Barrel: 5"
Finish: Blued, nickel, parkerized, or similar finish, checkered walnut grips; adopted as U.S. military side arm in 1911
Estimated Value: $380.00 - $475.00

Colt Commercial Model 1911
Same as Government Model 1911 except: not marked with military markings; blued or nickel finish; the letter "C" is used in serial numbers.
Estimated Value: $425.00 - $550.00

Colt 1911
Springfield Armory N.R.A.
Same general specifications as Goverment 1911 Colt; approximately 200 were made prior to World War I and sold through the Director of Civilian Marksmanship with N.R.A. markings on frame
Estimated Value: $1,800.00 - $2,200.00

Colt 1911
(North American Arms Co.)
Same general specifications as Goverment 1911 Colt; made by North American Arms Co. in World War I period; about 100 made
Estimated Value: $4,000.00 - $5,000.00

Colt 1911 (Springfield Armory)
Same general specifications as Goverment 1911 Colt except approximately 26,000 were produced; eagle motif and flaming bomb on frame and slide; made in World War I period
Estimated Value: $500.00 - $650.00

Colt 1911 (Remington UMC)
Same general specifications as Goverment 1911 Colt; approximately 22,000 were produced in World War I period
Estimated Value: $450.00 - $600.00

Colt 1911 (by Remington UMC)

Colt Government Model 1911 A1
Same as Government Model 1911 except: the grip safety tang was lengthened (to stop the hammer bite on fleshy hands); the trigger was shortened (to allow stubby fingers better control); the back strap below the grip safety was arched (for better instinctive pointing); the sights were made larger & squared (to improve sight picture)
Estimated Value: $365.00 - $460.00

Colt Commercial Model 1911 A1
Same as Government Model 1911 except it has same modifications as the Government Model 1911 A1
Estimated Value: $320.00 - $420.00

Colt Super 38
Same as Colt Commercial Model 1911 A1 except: 38 Super ACP caliber; 9-shot clip
Estimated Value: $400.00 - $500.00

Colt Super 38 Match
Same as Colt Super 38 except: adjustable rear sight; hand-honed action; match grade barrel
Estimated Value: $480.00 - $600.00

Colt National Match
Same as Colt Commercial Model 1911 A1 except: adjustable rear sight; hand-honed action; match grade barrel
Estimated Value: $550.00 - $690.00

Colt 1911 A1 (Singer Manufacturing Co.)
Same general specifications as Goverment 1911 A1 Colt; approximately 500 made; blued finished, slide marked S.M. Co.
Estimated Value: $2,600.00 - $3,200.00

Colt 1911 A1 pistols were also produced during World War II by Union Switch & Signal Company, Remington Rand, Inc. and Ithaca Gun Company, Inc. Generally, the estimated values of these pistols are about the same as the 1911 A1 pistol produced by Colt.

Colt Super 38

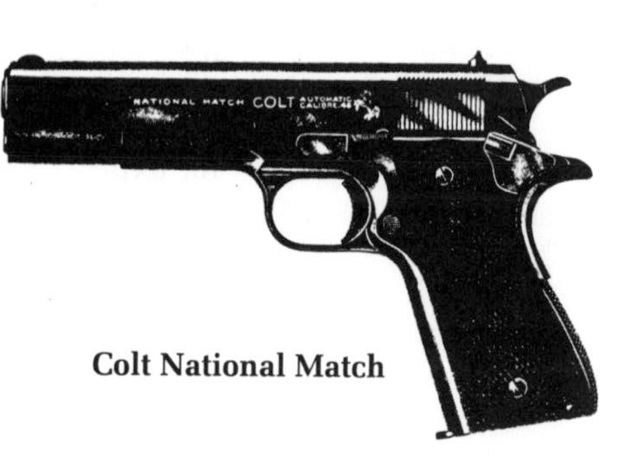

Colt National Match

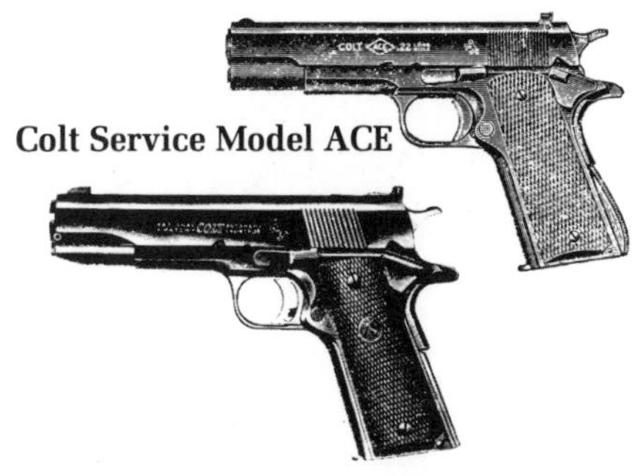

Colt Service Model ACE

Colt Gold Cup National Match

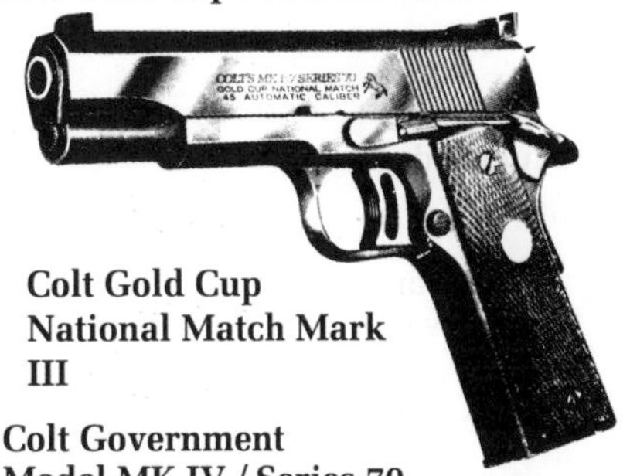

Colt Gold Cup National Match Mark III

Colt Service Model Ace
Similar to Colt National Match except: 22 caliber long rifle; 10-shot clip; It has a "floating chamber" that makes the recoil much greater than normal 22 caliber. (See Colt Ace *current.*)
Estimated Value: $800.00 - $1,000.00

Colt Gold Cup National Match
Same as Colt Commercial Model 1911 A1 except: hand fitted slide; enlarged ejection port; adjustable rear sight; adjustable trigger stop; new bushing design; checkered walnut grips; match grade barrel; flat grip below safety like model 1911
Estimated Value: $420.00 - $525.00

Colt Gold Cup National Match III
Similar to Colt Gold Cup National Match except chambered for 38 Special mid-range wad cutter only; operates with fixed barrel rather than locked breech
Estimated Value: $400.00 - $500.00

Colt Government Model MK IV / Series 70
Caliber: 9mm Parabellum, 38 Super ACP, 45 ACP
Action: Semi-automatic; exposed spur hammer
Magazine: 9-shot clip in 9mm & 38; 7-shot in 45
Barrel: 5"
Finish: Blued or nickel; smooth or checkered walnut grips
Estimated Value: $300.00 - $375.00

Colt Gold Cup MK IV National Match (Series 70)
Caliber: 38 Special Mid-Range, 45 ACP
Action: Semi-automatic; exposed spur hammer; arched or flat back strap; adjustable trigger stop, hand-fitted slide, and improved barrel bushing
Magazine: 9-shot clip in 38; 7-shot in 45
Barrel: 5"
Finish: Blued; checkered walnut grips with gold medallion.
Estimated Value: $380.00 - $475.00

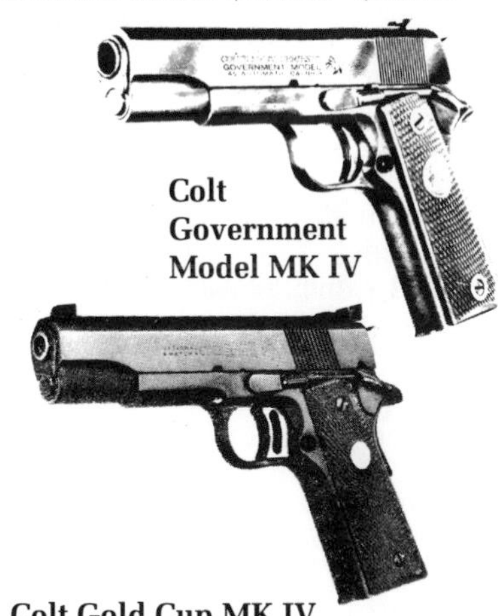

Colt Government Model MK IV

Colt Gold Cup MK IV National Match

Semi-automatics

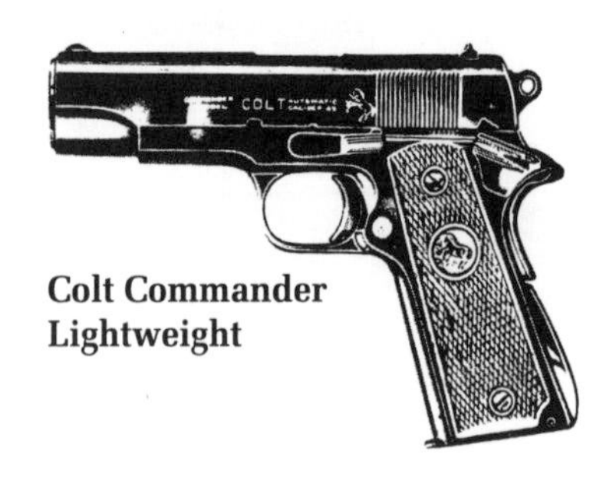

Colt Commander Lightweight

Colt Commander Lightweight
Caliber: 45 ACP
Action: Semi-automatic; exposed round spur hammer; Same design as Gov. 1911 A1 model except shorter and lighter; alloy frame
Magazine: 7-shot clip
Barrel: 4¼"
Finish: Blued; checkered or smooth walnut grips
Estimated Value: $280.00 - $350.00

Colt Combat Commander

Colt Combat Commander
Caliber: 9mm Parabellum, 38 Super ACP, 45 ACP
Action: Semi-automatic; exposed round hammer; steel frame with flat or arched back strap Same design as Government 1911 A1 model except: shorter and lighter
Magazine: 9-shot clip in 9mm and 38 Super; 7-shot clip in 45 ACP
Barrel: 4¼"
Finish: Blued or nickel (in 45 caliber only); checkered walnut grips; add 10% for nickel finish
Estimated Value: $300.00 - $375.00

Colt Ace Target
Caliber: 22 long rifle
Action: Semi-automatic; exposed spur hammer; thumb and grip safeties
Magazine: 10-shot clip
Barrel: 4¾"
Finish: Blued; checkered walnut or plastic grips
Estimated Value: $640.00 - $800.00

Colt Combat Commander Series 80
Similar to the Combat Commander with internal improvements; add 5% for nickel finish; add 10% for stainless steel finish
Estimated Value: $385.00 - $480.00

Colt Ace (Later)
Caliber: 22 long rifle
Action: Semi-automatic; exposed spur hammer
Magazine: 10-shot clip
Barrel: 5"
Finish: Blued; checkered walnut grips
Estimated Value: $320.00 - $400.00

Colt Ace Target

Colt Commander Lightweight Series 80
Similar to the Lightweight Commander with internal improvements
Estimated Value: $385.00 - $480.00

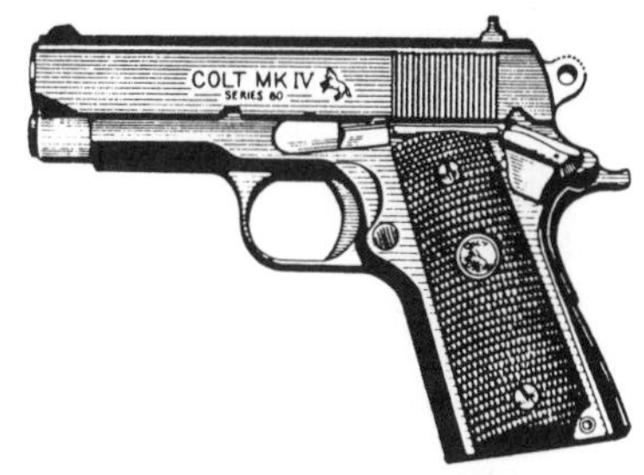

Colt MK IV Series 80 Officer's ACP

Colt MK IV Series 80 Officer's ACP
Caliber: 45 ACP
Action: Semi-automatic; exposed round spur hammer
Magazine: 6-shot clip
Barrel: 3½"
Finish: Non-glare matte blue, blued or stainless steel; add 10% for stainless steel; checkered wood grips; A compact 45 ACP pistol
Estimated Value: $375.00 - $470.00

Colt Government Model MK IV/Series 80
Similar to the MK IV Series 70 with internal improvements; add 8% for nickel finish; add 10% for stainless steel
Estimated Value: $385.00 - $480.00

Colt Combat Government Model/80
Similar to the Government MK IV/Series 80 with undercut front sight, outline rear sight, Colt Pachmayr grips and other slight variations
Estimated Value: $355.00 - $475.00

Colt Gold Cup National Match MK IV/Series 80
Similar to the Gold Cup MK IV National Match (Series 70) with internal improvements, 45 caliber only; add 10% for stainless steel
Estimated Value: $490.00 - $615.00

Colt Government Model MK IV/Series 80

Semi-automatics

Colt 380 Government Model, MK IV Series 80
A "scaled down" version of the Colt Government Model MK IV Series 80 in 380 ACP caliber; with round spur hammer; 3¼" barrel; add 10% for stainless steel finish
Estimated Value: $250.00 - $315.00

Colt 380 Government Pocketlite
Similar to the 380 Government Model, MK IV Series 80 with alloy receiver and blued finish
Estimated Value: $250.00 - $315.00

Colt MK IV Series 80 Mustang 380

Colt Combat Elite
Caliber: 45ACP
Action: Semi-automatic; exposed round combat hammer
Magazine: 7-shot clip
Barrel: 5"
Finish: Matte stainless steel receiver with blued carbon steel slide; black Neoprene "pebbled" wrap-around combat-style grips
Estimated Value: $465.00 - $580.00

Colt 380 Government Model

Colt MK IV Series 80 Mustang 380
Caliber: 380 ACP
Action: Semi-automatic; exposed round spur hammer
Magazine: 5-shot clip
Barrel: 2¾"
Finish: Blued; nickel, electroless nickel or stainless steel; composition grips; add 10% for nickel or stainless steel
Estimated Value: $250.00 - $315.00

Colt MK IV Series 80 Mustang Plus II
Similar to the Mustang 380 but combines the full grip length of the Colt Government Model with the shorter compact barrel and slide of the Mustang; add 10% for stainless steel
Estimated Value: $250.00 - $305.00

Colt MK IV Series 80 Mustang Pocketlite
Similar to the Mustang 380 with an alloy receiver; Blued only
Estimated Value: $250.00 - $315.00

Colt MK IV Series 80 Mustang Plus II

Colt Delta Elite

Colt Delta Elite, MK IV Series 80
Caliber: 10mm
Action: Semi-automatic; exposed round hammer; long trigger
Magazine: 7-shot clip
Barrel: 5"
Finish: Blued or stainless steel; black Neoprene "pebbled" wrap-around combat-style grips
Estimated Value: $425.00 - $530.00

Colt Double Eagle Series 90
Caliber: 45ACP, 10mm; 9mm and 38 Super
Action: Double action semi-automatic with exposed combat style rounded hammer; a decocking lever allows the hammer to be decocked with a round in the chamber.
Magazine: 8-shot clip
Barrel: 5"
Finish: Matte stainless steel; checkered Xenoy grips
Estimated Value: $415.00 - $520.00

Colt Dougle Eagle Series 90

Colt Double Eagle
Combat Commander
Similar to the Double Eagle in 45 ACP or 40 S&W caliber; 4¼" barrel
Estimated Value: $415.00 - $520.00

Colt Double Eagle Officer's Model
Similar to the Double Eagle with 3½" barrel, stainless steel or blued finish
Estimated Value: $415.00 - $520.00

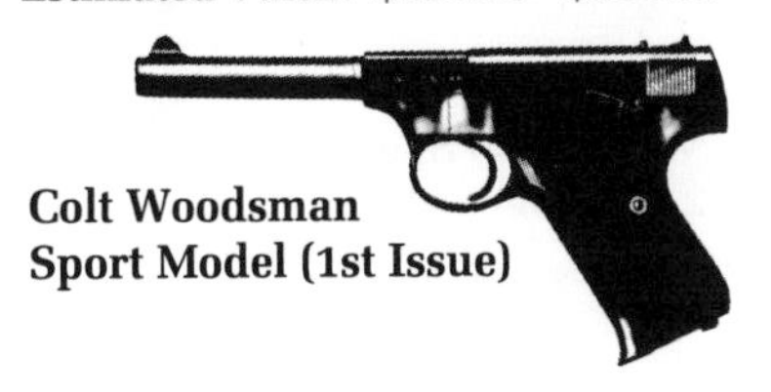
Colt Woodsman
Sport Model (1st Issue)

Colt Woodsman
Sport Model (1st Issue)
Caliber: 22 long rifle
Action: Semi-automatic; concealed hammer
Magazine: 10-shot clip
Barrel: 4½" tapered barrel
Finish: Blued; checkered walnut grips
Estimated Value: $300.00 - $375.00

Semi-automatics

Colt Woodsman Target Model (1st Issue)

Colt Woodsman
Target Model (1st Issue)
Caliber: 22 long rifle (regular velocity)
Action: Semi-automatic; concealed hammer
Magazine: 10-shot clip
Barrel: 6½"
Finish: Blued; checkered walnut grips
Estimated Value: $310.00 - $390.00

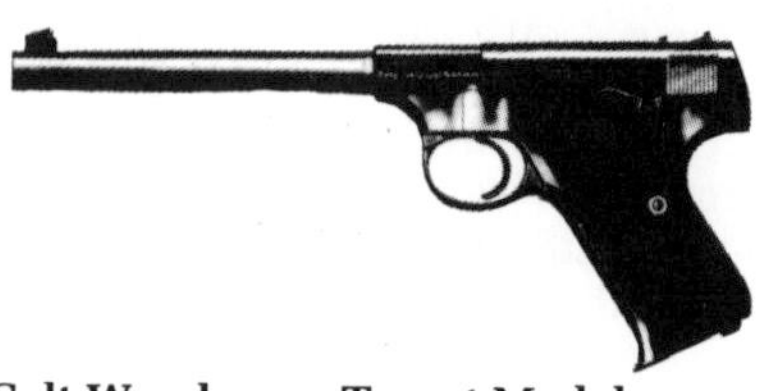

Colt Woodsman Target Model (2nd Issue)

Colt Woodsman
Target Model (2nd Issue)
Same as Colt Woodsman Target Model 1st Issue except heavier tapered barrel and stronger housing for using either the 22 long rifle regular or Hi-speed cartridges.
Estimated Value: $320.00 - $400.00

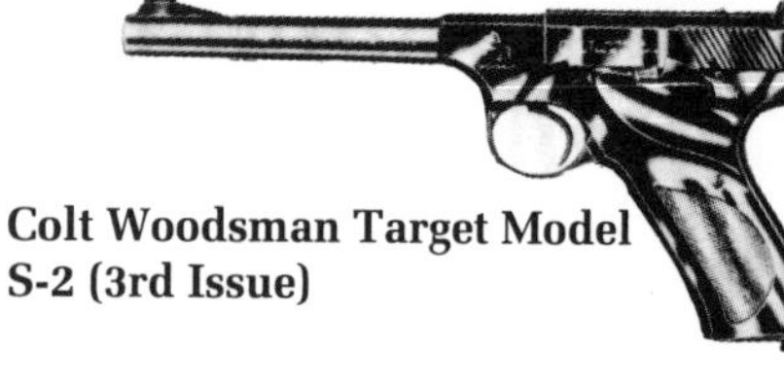

Colt Woodsman Target Model S-2 (3rd Issue)

Colt Woodsman
Target Model S-2 (3rd Issue)
Same as Colt Woodsman Target Model (2nd Issue) except longer grips with thumb rest; slide stop; checkered walnut or plastic grips
Estimated Value: $260.00 - $325.00

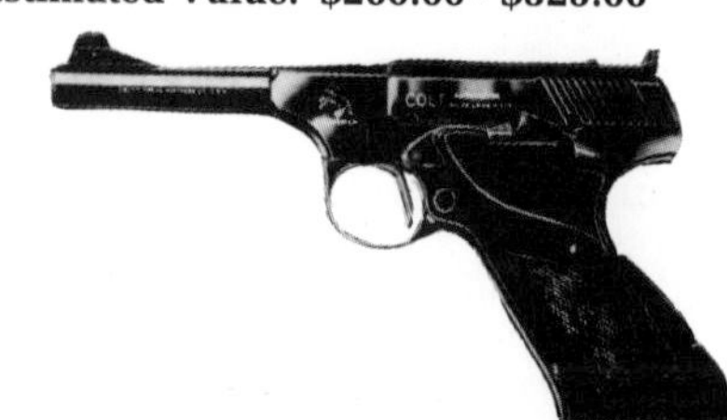

Colt Woodsman Sport Model S-1 (2nd Issue)

Colt Woodsman
Sport Model S-1 (2nd Issue)
Same as Colt Woodsman Target Model S-2 (3rd Issue) except 4½" barrel
Estimated Value: $255.00 - $320.00

Colt Model S-4 Targetsman
Similar to Colt Woodsman Target Model (3rd Issue) except cheaper made, lacks automatic slide stop.
Estimated Value: $200.00 - $250.00

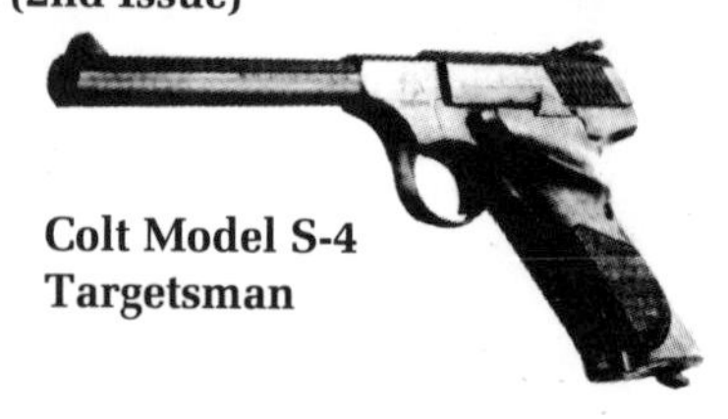

Colt Model S-4 Targetsman

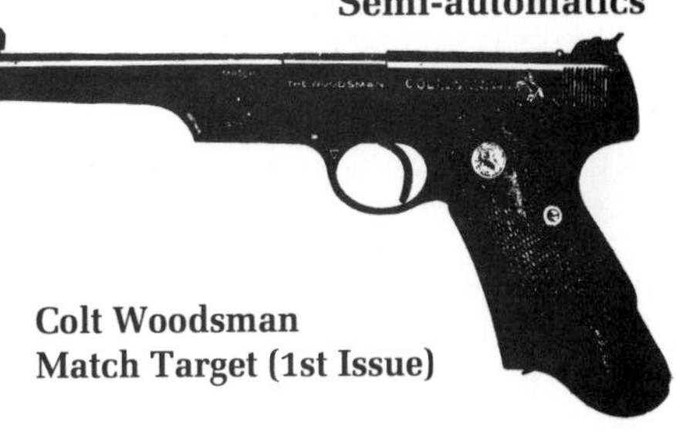
Colt Woodsman Match Target (1st Issue)

Colt Woodsman Match Target (1st Issue)
Caliber: 22 long rifle
Action: Semi-automatic; concealed hammer
Magazine: 10-shot clip
Barrel: 6½"; slightly tapered with flat sides
Finish: Blued; checkered walnut, one-piece grip with extended sides
Estimated Value: $475.00 - $600.00

Colt Woodsman Match Target Model S-3

Colt Woodsman Match Target Model S-3
Caliber: 22 long rifle
Action: Semi-automatic; concealed hammer
Magazine: 10-shot clip
Barrel: 4½", 6"
Finish: Blued; checkered walnut grips with thumb rest Flat sided weight full-length of barrel; slide stop and maazine safety
Estimated Value: $265.00 - $330.00

Colt Huntsman Model S-5
Caliber: 22 long rifle
Action: Semi-automatic; concealed hammer
Magazine: 10-shot clip
Barrel: 4½", 6"
Finish: Blued; checkered walnut grips
Estimated Value: $210.00 - $260.00

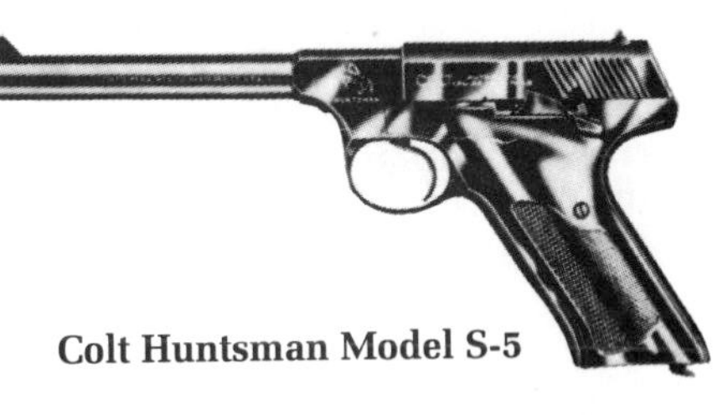
Colt Huntsman Model S-5

Colt Challenger Model
Caliber: 22 long rifle
Action: Semi-automatic; concealed hammer
Magazine: 10-shot clip
Barrel: 4½", 6"
Finish: Blued; checkered plastic grip; slide doesn't stay open when magazine is empty; no magazine safety
Estimated Value: $200.00 - $250.00

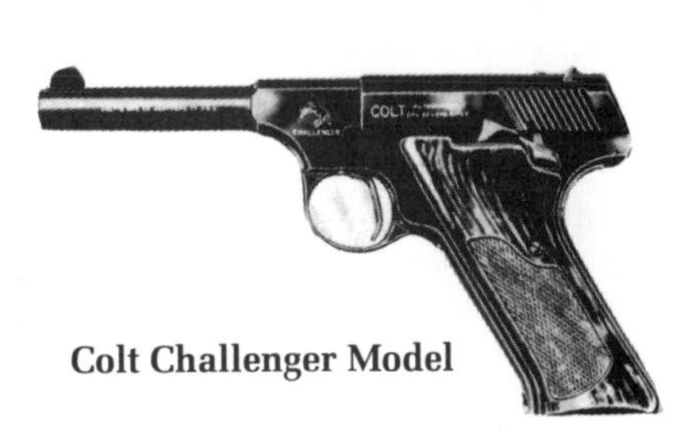
Colt Challenger Model

Dardick

Dardick Magazine Pistol
David Dardick developed a handgun, which resembles an automatic pistol, around a new type of cartridge called the "tround." The tround has a triangular case made of plastic. For the 38 caliber, the primer, powder, & bullets are loaded into the tround. The 22 caliber cartridges are simply placed in a plastic tround to adapt them to the feeding system. The firing pin position is changed to rimfire by manually turning a screw in the frame. Therefore, the basic gun will shoot 22 caliber or 38 caliber by changing the barrel. The feeding system used a three-legged star wheel which moves from magazine to firing position & dumps rounds through opening on right side. The feeding system is moved 120° with each pull of the trigger. The magazine is loaded by placing trounds in singly or by using 10-shot stripper clips. Production was started in 1959 in Hamden, Connecticut & ceased in 1960. All facilities, guns, & parts were auctioned to Numrich Arms in 1960. Approximately 40 guns were produced. The gun was made in three models & a rifle conversion kit. All models were made with two barrels (22 and 38 caliber).

Dardick 1100 - 11 shot
Dardick 1500 - 15 shot
Dardick 2000 - 20 shot

All models could be converted to a rifle by removing the barrel & fitting the frame into the rifle conversion kit.

Dardick Magazine Pistol

Estimated Value:
Pistol with 22 & 38 caliber barrels
$375.00 - $500.00
Pistol with 22 & 38 caliber barrels & rifle conversion kit
$960.00 - $1,200.00

Desert Eagle

Desert Eagle

Desert Eagle, Mark I, Mark VII
Caliber: 357 magnum; 44 magnum (in 1986); 41 magnum (in 1989); 50 Action Express (1992)
Action: Gas operated semi-automatic; single action; exposed hammer; rotating locking bolt
Magazine: 9-shot clip (357 magnum); 8-shot clip (44 magnum)
Barrel: 6" standard; 10" or 14" available
Finish: Black oxide, blued, satin nickel, or bright nickel; wrap-around rubber grips; alloy frame or stainless steel frame; add 6% for 44 magnum; add 17% for 41 magnum; 6% for stainless steel frame; add 24% for 10" barrel or 14" barrel
Estimated Value: $475.00 - $590.00

Detonics

Detonics Mark I, Combat Master
Caliber: 45 ACP; 9mm; 38 Super ACP
Action: Semi-automatic; exposed hammer; single action; thumb safety
Magazine: 6-shot clip
Barrel: 3¼"
Finish: Polished blue or matte blue; walnut grips
Estimated Value: $550.00 - $690.00

Detonics Combat Master

Detonics Mark V, Combat Master
Similar to the Mark I except matte stainless steel finish
Estimated Value: $480.00 - $600.00

Detonics Mark VI, Combat Master
Similar to the Mark V except polished stainless steel
Estimated Value: $485.00 - $605.00

Detonics Scoremaster

Detonics Service Master
Similar to the Combat Master except slightly longer and heavier, Millett sights, dull finish.
Estimated Value: $600.00 - $750.00

Detonics Scoremaster
Similar to the Combat Master with a 5" or 6" barrel, 7 or 8-shot clip; 45 ACP or 451 Detonics magnum; add $40.00 for 6" barrel
Estimated Value: $ 700.00 - $ 880.00

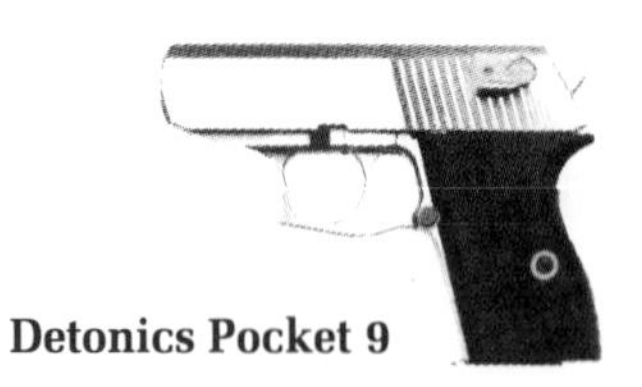
Detonics Pocket 9

Detonics Pocket 9
Caliber: 9 mm
Action: Double and single action, blowback; semi-automatic
Magazine: 6-shot clip
Barrel: 3"
Finish: Matte finish stainless steel, hooked and serrated trigger guard
Estimated Value: $320.00 - $400.00

Glock

Glock 17

Glock 17, 17L, 19
Caliber: 9mm (9mmx19mm) (Parabellum) Luger
Action: Recoil operated semi-automatic; double action
Magazine: 17 shot clip (17 & 17L), 15 shot (19) or an opt. 19 or 17 shot clip
Barrel: 4½" (17), 6" (17L), or 4" (19)
Finish: Space-age polymer & machined steel; the 17L has cut away slide top; add 45% for 17L
Estimated Value: $350.00 - $435.00

Glock 20

Glock 20, 21
Similar to the 19 except: 10mm and 45 ACP calibers; 4½" barrel
Estimated Value: $380.00 - $480.00

Glock 22, 23
Similar to the 20, 21 except 40 S&W caliber, 13 or 15-shot clip
Estimated Value: $350.00 - $435.00

Glock 22

Harrington & Richardson

H & R Self Loading 25
Caliber: 25 ACP
Action: Semi-automatic; concealed hammer
Magazine: 6-shot clip; simultaneous ejector
Barrel: 2"
Finish: Blued; hard rubber grips
Estimated Value: $225.00 - $280.00

H&R Self Loading 25

H & R Self Loading 32
Caliber: 32 ACP
Action: Semi-automatic; concealed hammer; grip safety
Magazine: 8-shot clip
Barrel: 3½"
Finish: Blued; hard rubber grips
Estimated Value: $210.00 - $265.00

Hartford

Hartford Automatic Target
Caliber: 22 long rifle
Action: Semi-automatic; concealed hammer
Magazine: 10-shot clip
Barrel: 6¾"
Finish: Blued; black rubber grips
Estimated Value: $300.00 - $375.00

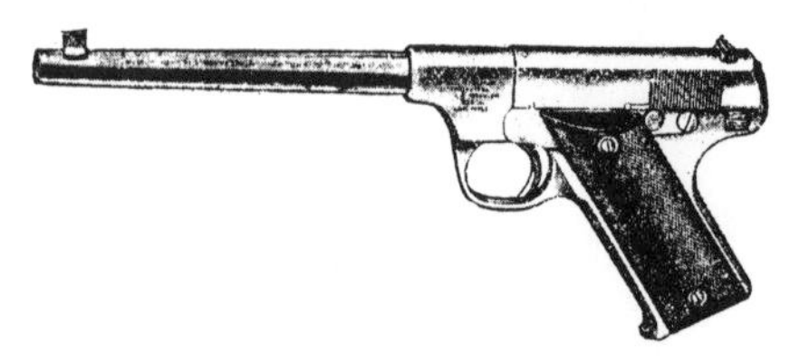

Hartford Automatic Target

Hartford Repeating Pistol
Caliber: 22 long rifle
Action: Manual operation of slide after each shot to eject cartridge & feed another cartridge from magazine to chamber; concealed hammer
Magazine: 10-shot clip
Barrel: 6¾"
Finish: Blued; black rubber grips
Estimated Value: $300.00 - $400.00

Heckler & Koch

Heckler & Koch Model P7

Heckler & Koch Model P7 (M-8, M-13 & K-3)
Caliber: 9mm Parabellum; 380 ACP (K-3 added 1988)
Action: Recoil operated semi-automatic; concealed hammer; contains a unique system of cocking by squeezing front of grips, uncocking by releasing; double action
Magazine: 8-shot clip (M-8 & K-3); 13-shot (M-13); add 25% for M-13
Barrel: 4⅛"
Finish: Blued; black grips
Estimated Value: $545.00 - $680.00

Heckler & Koch Model P9S
Caliber: 9mm Parabellum; 45 ACP
Action: Semi-automatic; concealed hammer; cocking lever
Magazine: 9-shot clip; 7-shot clip in 45 ACP
Barrel: 4"
Finish: Blued; black plastic grips; wood combat grips available
Estimated Value: $780.00 - $975.00

Heckler & Koch Model P9S

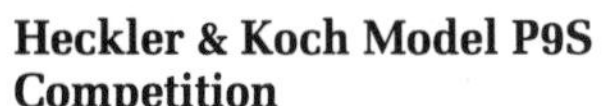

Heckler & Koch Model P9S Competition
Similar to the Model P9S Target with both 4" & 5½" barrels, 2 slides, wood competition grips and plastic grips, all packed in a special case; 9mm only
Estimated Value: $725.00 - $1,000.00

Heckler & Koch Model P9S Target
Similar to the Model P9S except adjustable trigger, trigger stop & adjustable rear sight; 5½" barrel available
Estimated Value: $830.00 - $1,035.00

Heckler & Koch Model HK4

Heckler & Koch Model HK4
Caliber: 380; conversion kits available for calibers 38, 25, and 22 long rifle; add $160.00 for all three conversion kits
Action: Semi-automatic; double action; exposed hammer spur
Magazine: 7-shot clip
Barrel: 3⅜"
Finish: Blued; black plactic grips; grip extension on clip;
Estimated Value: $240.00 - $320.00

Heckler & Koch Model VP70Z
Caliber: 9mm
Action: Semi-automatic; blow back, recoil operated; double action only; hammerless
Magazine: Double stacked 18-shot clip; 2 magazines standard
Barrel: 4½"
Finish: Blued; black plastic grips; solid plastic receiver
Estimated Value: $260.00 - $325.00

High Standard

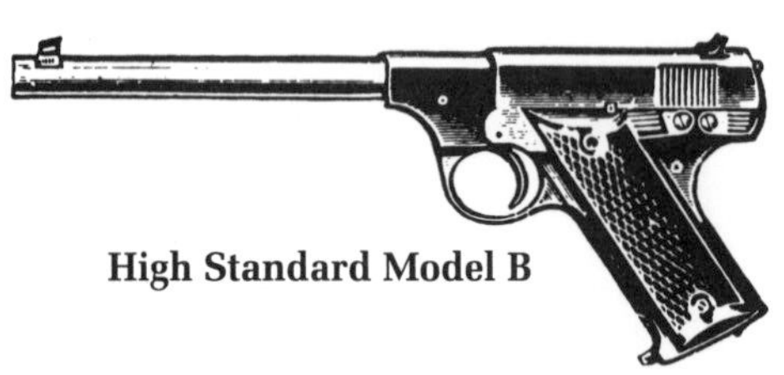

High Standard Model B

High Standard Model B
Caliber: 22 long rifle
Action: Semi-automatic; concealed hammer; thumb safety
Magazine: 10-shot clip
Barrel: 4½" or 6¾"
Finish: Blued; hard rubber grips
Estimated Value: $200.00 - $250.00

High Standard Model HB
Same as Model B except exposed hammer & no thumb safety
Estimated Value: $210.00 - $260.00

High Standard Model C
Same as Model B except chambered for 22 short cartridges
Estimated Value: $180.00 - $225.00

High Standard Model SB
Same as Model B except 6¾" smooth bore for shooting 22 long rifle shot cartridges.
Estimated Value: $160.00 - $200.00

High Standard Model A
Caliber: 22 long rifle
Action: Semi-automatic; concealed hammer; thumb safety
Magazine: 10-shot clip
Barrel: 4½" or 6¾"
Finish: Blued; checkered walnut grips
Estimated Value: $220.00 - $270.00

High Standard Model A

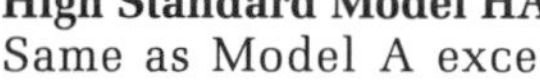

High Standard Model HA
Same as Model A except exposed hammer & no thumb safety
Estimated Value: $225.00 - $275.00

High Standard Model D

Same as Model A except heavier barrel
Estimated Value: $220.00 - $275.00

High Standard Model HD
Same as Model D except exposed hammer & no thumb safety
Estimated Value: $225.00 - $280.00

High Standard Model HD

High Standard Model HDM or HD Military
Same as Model HD except it has thumb safety; stamped "U.S. Property"
Estimated Value: $260.00 - $325.00

High Standard Model HD Military (Postwar)
Same as Model HDM except it is not stamped "U.S. Property"
Estimated Value: $225.00 - $280.00

High Standard Model E
Similar to Model A except extra heavy barrel; thumb rest grips
Estimated Value: $220.00 - $275.00

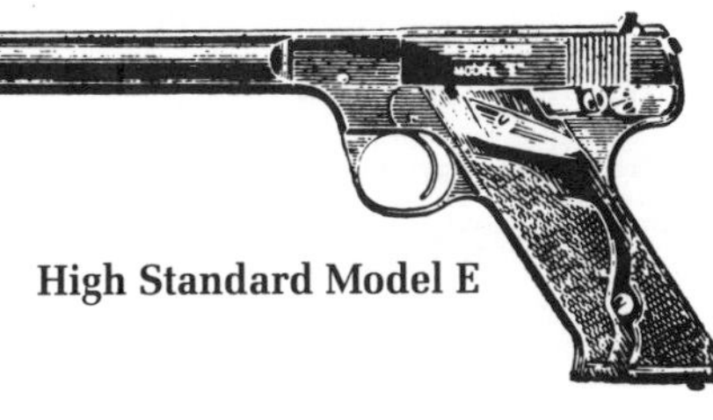

High Standard Model E

High Standard Model HE
Same as Model E except exposed hammer & no thumb safety
Estimated Value: $215.00 - $270.00

High Standard G-B

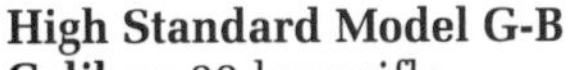

High Standard Model G-B
Caliber: 22 long rifle
Action: Semi-automatic; concealed hammer; takedown model; interchangeable barrels; thumb safety
Magazine: 10-shot clip
Barrel: 4½" or 6¾"; add $50.00 for pistol with both barrels
Finish: Blued; checkered plastic grips
Estimated Value: $170.00 - $210.00

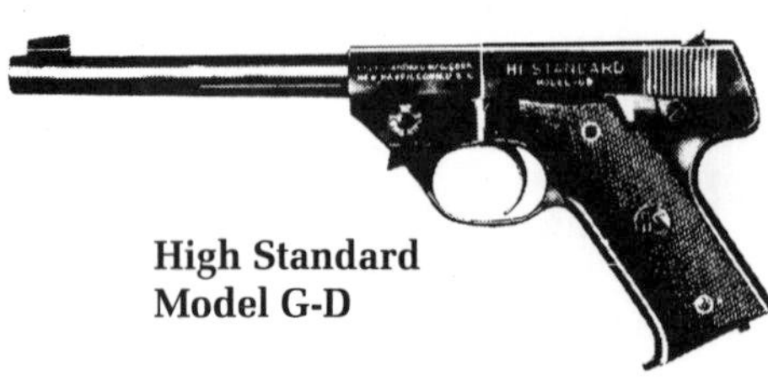
High Standard Model G-D

High Standard Model G-D
Same as Model G-B except: adjustable target sights; checkered walnut grips; add $50.00 if pistol has both barrels
Estimated Value: $175.00 - $220.00

High Standard Model G-E
Same as Model G-D except: heavy barrel; thumb rest; walnut grips; add $50.00 if pistol has both barrels
Estimated Value: $200.00 - $250.00

High Standard Olympic 1st Model
Same as Model G-E except 22 short caliber; light alloy slide; add $50.00 if pistol has both barrels
Estimated Value: $260.00 - $325.00

High Standard Olympic 1st Model

High Standard Olympic 2nd Model
Same as Olympic 1st Model except: thumb safety located at center top of left grip; plastic grips with thumb rest; add $50.00 if pistol has both barrels
Estimated Value: $240.00 - $300.00

High Standard Olympic 2nd Model

High Standard Olympic ISU
Caliber: 22 short
Action: Semi-automatic; concealed hammer; wide target trigger; anti-backlash trigger adjustment
Magazine: 10-shot clip
Barrel: 5½" bull barrel; 8" tapered barrel; 6¾" tapered barrel; integral stabilizer & 2 removable weights
Finish: Blued; checkered walnut grips with thumb rests; regular Hi-Standard style grip or the squared military style grip
Estimated Value: $260.00 - $320.00

High Standard Olympic ISU

High Standard Model G-380
Caliber: 380 ACP
Action: Semi-automatic; exposed hammer; thumb safety; barrel take-down model
Magazine: 6-shot clip; bottom release
Barrel: 5"
Finish: Blued; checkered plastic grips
Estimated Value: $260.00 - $325.00

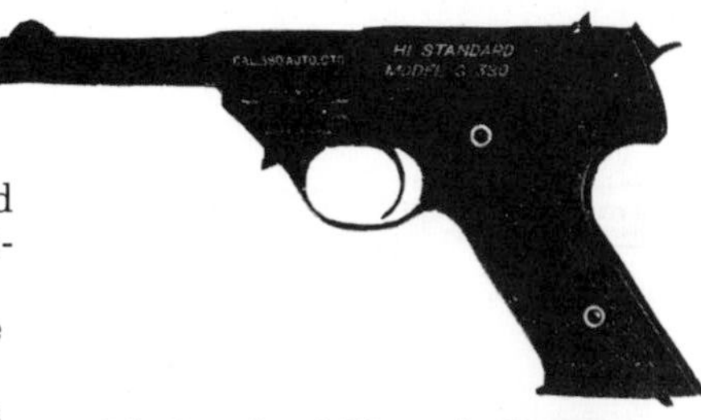

High Standard Olympic G-380

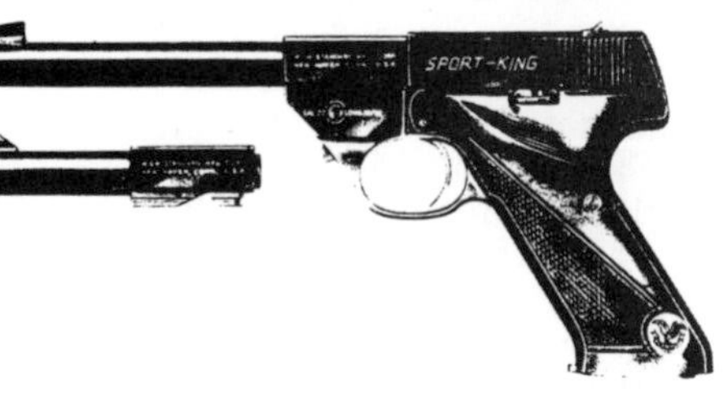

High Standard Sport-King 1st Model

High Standard Sport-King 1st Model
Caliber: 22 long rifle
Action: Semi-automatic; concealed hammer; takedown model with interchangeable barrel; thumb safety at top center of left grip; add $50.00 for pistol with both barrels
Magazine: 10-shot clip
Barrel: 4½" &/or 6¾"
Finish: Blued; checkered plastic grips with thumb rest.
Estimated Value: $160.00 - $200.00

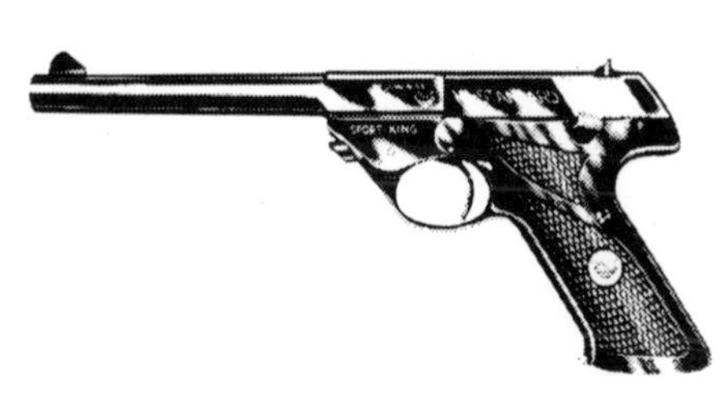

High Standard Sport-King 2nd Model

High Standard Sport-King 2nd Model
Similar to Sport-King 1st Model except: interior changes; blued or nickel finish; add $15.00 for nickel finish; add $50.00 for both barrels
Estimated Value: $170.00 - $210.00

High Standard Lightweight Sport-King
Same as Sport-King 1st Model except: aluminum alloy frame; add $50.00 for pistol with both barrels
Estimated Value: $150.00 - $195.00

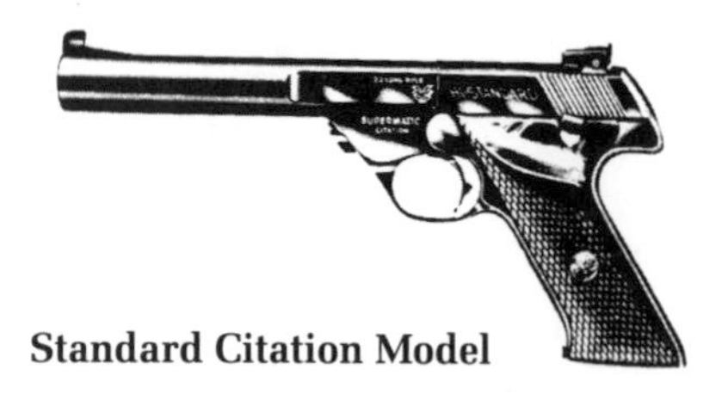

Standard Citation Model

High Standard Supermatic Series
Caliber: 22 long rifle
Action: Semi-automatic; concealed hammer; thumb safety; takedown model with interchangeable barrels
Magazine: 10-shot clip
Barrel: 4½", 5½", 6¾" 7¼", 8", or 10"; the 5¼" barrel is heavy (bull) barrel & the 7¼" barrel is heavy (bull) fluted barrel
Finish: Blued; checkered plastic or checkered wood grips with or without thumb rest

Standard Supermatic Model
4¼" or 6¾" interchangeable barrels; add $50.00 for pistol with both barrels
Estimated Value: 175.00 - $220.00

Supermatic Tournament Model
5½" bull barrel or 6¾" regular barrel with stabilizer & 2 removable weights; adjustable trigger pull; add $50.00 for pistol with both barrels
Estimated Value: $240.00 - $300.00

Supermatic Citation Model
5½" bull barrel or 6¾", 8" or 10" tapered barrel with stabilizer & 2 removable weights; adjustable trigger pull
Estimated Value: $220.00 - $275.00

High Standard Flite-King 1st Model
Same as Sport-King 1st Model except: aluminum alloy frame and slide; 22 short caliber only; add $50.00 for pistol with both barrels
Estimated Value: $150.00 - $190.00

High Standard Flite-King 2nd Model
Same as Sport-King 1st Model except: all steel construction; 22 long rifle only; add $50.00 for pistol with both barrels
Estimated Value: $160.00 - $200.00

High Standard Field-King
Same as Sport-King 1st Model except: adjustable target sights; 6¾" heavy barrel
Estimated Value: $160.00 - $200.00

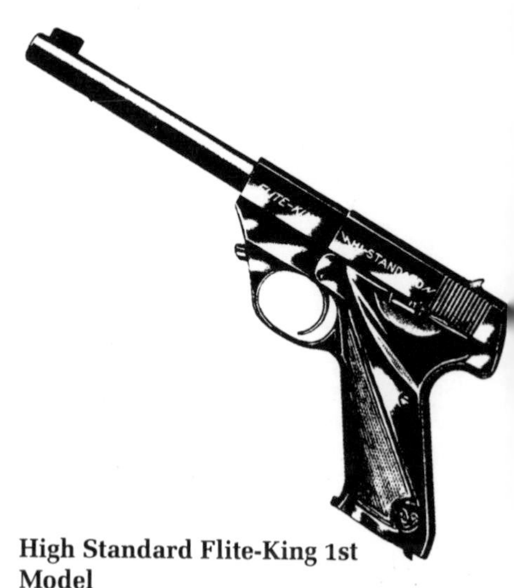

High Standard Flite-King 1st Model

Supermatic Citation, Military or Citation II
5½" heavy (bull) barrel or 7¼" heavy fluted barrel with military grip or standard grip; 5½" or 7¼" slabbed barrel after 1983 (Citation II)
Estimated Value: $235.00 - $290.00

Supermatic Trophy Citation
5½" bull barrel or 7¼" heavy fluted barrel
Estimated Value: $240.00 - $300.00

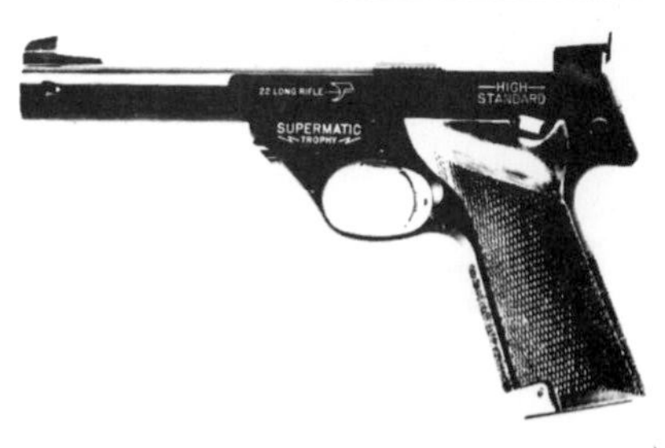

Supermatic Trophy Military Model
5½" bull barrel or 7¼" fluted barrel with square military-style grip; adjustable trigger pull; add $50.00 for both barrels
Estimated Value: $250.00 - $320.00

Supermatic Trophy Military Model

High Standard Dura-Matic
Caliber: 22 long rifle
Action: Semi-automatic; concealed hammer; takedown interchangeable barrels
Magazine: 10-shot clip
Barrel: 4½", 6½"
Finish: Blued; checkered plastic grips
Estimated Value: $130.00 - $160.00

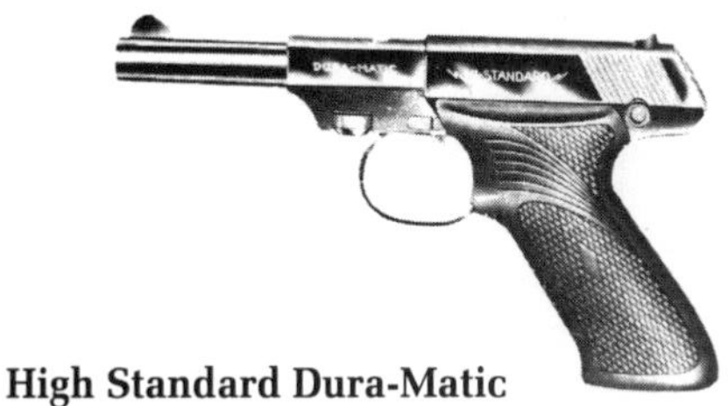

High Standard Dura-Matic

High Standard Plinker
Caliber: 22 long rifle
Action: Semi-automatic; concealed hammer
Magazine: 10-shot clip
Barrel: 4½", 6½"
Finish: Blued; checkered plastic grips
Estimated Value: $110.00 - $140.00

High Standard Plinker

High Standard Sharpshooter

High Standard Sharpshooter and Survival Pack
Caliber: 22 long rifle
Action: Semi-automatic; concealed hammer
Magazine: 10-shot clip
Barrel: 5½" bull barrel
Finish: Blued; checkered walnut grips; a survival pack consisting of a nickel pistol; extra magazine & canvas case available after 1982; add $75.00 for survival pack
Estimated Value: $200.00 - $250.00

High Standard 10-X

High Standard Victor
Caliber: 22 long rifle
Action: Semi-automatic; concealed hammer; interchangeable barrel
Magazine: 10-shot clip
Barrel: 4½" or 5½" with solid or aluminum ventilated rib & barrel weights
Finish: Blued; checkered walnut grips with thumb rest; Hi-Standard type grip or square military type grips
Estimated Value: $270.00 - $340.00

High Standard Victor

High Standard 10-X
Caliber: 22 long rifle
Action: Semi-automatic; concealed hammer; adjustable target trigger
Magazine: 10-shot clip; 2 extra standard
Barrel: 5½" bull barrel
Finish: Non-reflective blue; checkered walnut military grip; components hand picked & fitted by gunsmith; gunsmith's initials located under left grip
Estimated Value: $460.00 - $575.00

Iver Johnson

Iver Johnson X300 Pony, PO380, PO380B
Caliber: 380 ACP
Action: Single or double; semi-automatic; exposed hammer
Magazine: 6-shot clip
Barrel: 3"
Finish: Blued, nickel or military; checkered or smooth walnut grips; add 5% for nickel
Estimated Value: $160.00 - $215.00

Iver Johnson X300 Pony

Iver Johnson Model TP22

Iver Johnson Model TP22, TP25, TP22B, TB25B
Caliber: 22 long rifle (TP22), 25 ACP (TP25)
Action: Double action; semi-automatic; exposed hammer
Magazine: 7-shot clip
Barrel: 3"
Finish: Blued or nickel; plastic grips; finger extension on clip; add 8% for nickel
Estimated Value: $115.00 - $145.00

Iver Johnson Trailsman
Caliber: 22 long rifle
Action: Semi-automatic, concealed hammer
Magazine: Clip
Barrel: 4½"or 6"
Finish: Blued; checkered plastic or smooth hardwood grips
Estimated Value: $120.00 - $150.00

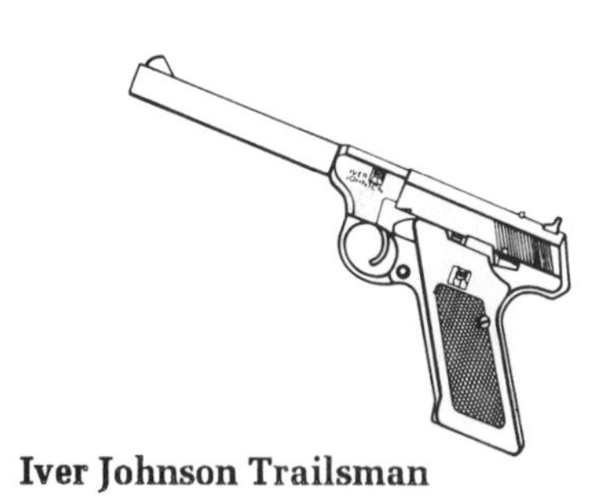

Iver Johnson Trailsman

Japanese

1904 Nambu Japanese
Caliber: 8mm bottle-necked Japanese
Action: Semi-automatic; grip safety below trigger guard
Magazine: 8-shot chip
Barrel: 4¾"
Finish: Blued; checkered wood grips; usually has a slot cut in rear of grip to accommodate shoulder stock holster; add $100.00 for shoulder stock holster
Estimated Value: $600.00 - $800.00

1904 Nambu Japanese

Baby Nambu Japanese
Caliber: 7mm bottle-necked Japanese cartridge
Action: Semi-automatic; grip safety below trigger guard
Magazine: 7-shot chip
Barrel: 3¼"
Finish: Blued; checkered wood grips; a smaller version of the 1904 Nambu
Estimated Value: $1,150.00 - $1,400.00

Baby Nambu Japanese

Type 57B New Nambu Japanese
Caliber: 32 ACP (7.65mm Browning)
Action: Semi-automatic; blowback operated
Magazine: 8-shot clip
Barrel: 3"
Finish: Blued; checkered grips; a modified copy of the Browning M1910 pistol
Estimated Value: $130.00 - $175.00

Type 26 Japanese
Caliber: 9mm rimmed pistol
Action: Double only; top break; hammer without spur
Magazine: 6-shot; automatic ejector
Barrel: 4¾"
Finish: Blued; checkered one-piece round grip
Estimated Value: $200.00 - $250.00

Nambu Type 14 Japanese
Caliber: 8mm bottle-necked Japanese
Action: Semi-automatic; manual safety
Magazine: 8-shot chip
Barrel: 4¾"
Finish: Blued; grooved wood grips
Estimated Value: $325.00 - $400.00

Modified Nambu Type 14 Japanese
Similar to Nambu Type 14 except it has enlarged trigger guard to allow use of heavy gloves & a spring mounted in lower front of grip to hold magazine more securely
Estimated Value: $335.00 - $425.00

Type 94 Japanese
Caliber: 8mm bottle-necked Japanese
Action: Semi-automatic
Magazine: 6-shot clip
Barrel: 3¾"
Finish: Blued; checkered grips
Estimated Value: $225.00 - $300.00

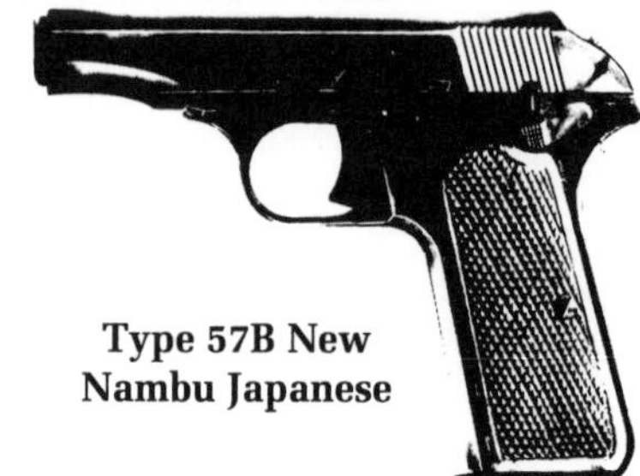

Type 57B New Nambu Japanese

Type 57 New Nambu Japanese
Caliber: 9mm Parabellum; 45 ACP
Action: Semi-automatic; recoil operated
Magazine: 8-shot clip
Barrel: 4½"
Finish: Blued; checkered grips; a modified copy of the U.S. 1911 A1; no grip safety; magazine catch at bottom of grip
Estimated Value: $150.00 - $200.00

Type 57 New Nambu Japanese

Lignose

Lignose Model 2 Pocket
Caliber: 25 ACP (6.35mm)
Action: Semi-automatic; concealed hammer, thumb safety at top rear of left grip
Magazine: 6-shot clip
Barrel: 2⅛"
Finish: Blued; checkered hard rubber grips; operation principle based on the 1906 Browning 25 automatic pocket pistol; made in Germany; early models marked "Bergmann"
Estimated Value: $200.00 - $250.00

Lignose Einhand Model 2A Pocket

Lignose Einhand Model 2A Pocket
Similar specifications as Model 2 except designed for one-hand operation, hence the name Einhand (one hand). Slide can be retracted to load & cock hammer, by using the trigger finger to pull back on the front part of the trigger guard
Estimated Value: $210.00 - $275.00

Lignose Einhand Model 3A Pocket
Same as Model 2A except: longer grip & uses 9-shot clip
Estimated Value: $225.00 - $300.00

Llama

Llama Model IX
Caliber: 45 ACP
Action: Semi-automatic; locked breech; exposed hammer; manual safety
Magazine: 7-shot clip
Barrel: 5"
Finish: Blued, checkered walnut grips
Estimated Value: $170.00 - $215.00

Llama Model IX

Llama Model IXA
Similar to Model IX except ventilated rib; modified & improved version; also in chrome & chrome engraved finish; add $40.00 for chrome, $50.00 for chrome engraved
Estimated Value: $170.00 - $225.00

Llama Model IIIA

Llama Model I
Caliber: 32 ACP (7.65mm)
Action: Semi-automatic; blowback-type; exposed hammer
Magazine: 8-shot clip
Barrel: 4"
Finish: Blued, wood grips
Estimated Value: $140.00 - $175.00

Llama Model IIIA
Caliber: 380 ACP
Action: Semi-automatic; manual & grip safety; exposed hammer
Magazine: 7-shot clip
Barrel: $3\frac{11}{16}$"
Finish: Blued, chrome, chrome engraved; plastic grips; ventilated rib; add $40.00 for chrome, $50.00 for engraved
Estimated Value: $150.00 - $200.00

Llama Model II
Similar to the Model I except 7-shot clip; caliber 380 ACP (9mm short)
Estimated Value: $150.00 - $185.00

Llama Model III
A modified version of the Model II
Estimated Value: $155.00 - $190.00

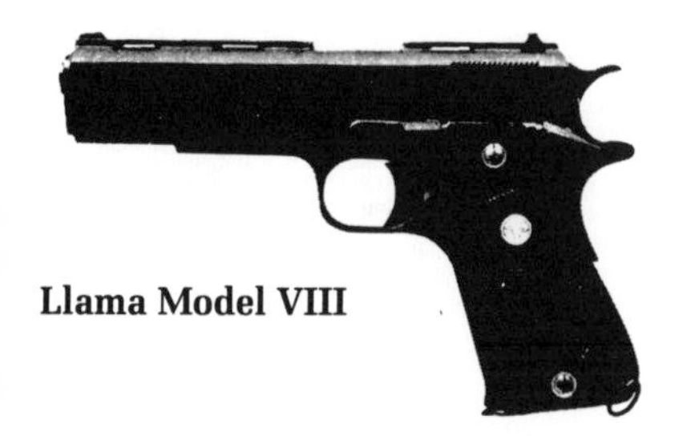
Llama Model VIII

Llama Model VIII
Caliber: 9mm Luger, 38 Super ACP
Action: Semi-automatic; manual & grip safety; exposed hammer
Magazine: 9-shot clip
Barrel: 5"
Finish: Blued, chrome, chrome engraved; checkered wood or simulated pearl grips; add $40.00 for chrome, $50.00 for engraved
Estimated Value: $220.00 - $275.00

Llama Model XI
Caliber: 9mm Luger
Action: Semi-automatic; manual safety; no grip safety; round exposed hammer
Magazine: 8-shot clip
Barrel: $4\frac{7}{8}$"
Finish: Blued, chrome; checkered plastic grips with modified thumb rest
Estimated Value: $190.00 - $250.00

Llama Model XI

Llama Model XV

Llama Model XV
Caliber: 22 long rifle
Action: Semi-automatic; blowback-type; exposed hammer; grip & manual safety.
Magazine: 9-shot clip
Barrel: $3\frac{11}{16}$"
Finish: Blued, chrome, or chrome engraved; checkered wood grips; a small version of the 1911 A1 Colt; add $40.00 for chrome, $50.00 for engraved
Estimated Value: $170.00 - $210.00

Llama Standard Automatic Small Frame
Similar to the Model XV, XA & IIIA; add 23% for chrome finish
Estimated Value: $195.00 - $240.00

Llama Model XA
Same as Model XV except caliber 32 ACP; 8-shot clip; add $40.00 for chrome
Estimated Value: $180.00 - $225.00

Semi-automatics

Llama Standard Automatic Large Frame
Similar to the Model VIII and IXA; add 30% for chrome finish
Estimated Value: $230.00 - $290.00

Llama Standard Automatic Compact
Similar to the Large Frame Model but scaled down; in 9mm and 45ACP; 7 or 9-shot clip; add 30% for chrome finish
Estimated Value: $230.00 - $290.00

Llama Model XVII

Llama M-82 DA
Caliber: 9mm
Action: Double action; semi-automatic
Magazine: 15-shot clip
Barrel: 4¼"
Finish: Blued, matte black polymer grips
Estimated Value: $585.00 - $730.00

Llama Omni
Caliber: 9mm Parabellum, 45 Auto
Action: Semi-automatic; double action; exposed hammer
Magazine: 13-shot clip in 9mm; 7-shot clip in 45
Barrel: 5"
Finish: Blued; checkered plastic grips
Estimated Value: $275.00 - $350.00

Llama Standard Automatic Large Frame

Llama Model XVII
Caliber: 22 short
Action: Semi-automatic; exposed hammer with round spur; manual safety
Magazine: 6-shot clip
Barrel: 2⅜"
Finish: Blued or chrome; plastic grips; add $20.00 for chrome
Estimated Value: $150.00 - $185.00

Llama Model XVIII
Same as Model XVII except: 32 ACP caliber; add $20.00 for chrome
Estimated Value: $160.00 - $195.00

Llama M-82 DA

MAB

MAB Model C

MAB Model A
Caliber: 25 ACP (6.35mm)
Action: Semi-automatic; concealed hammer; manual safety; blowback design
Magazine: 6-shot clip
Barrel: 2½"
Finish: Blued; checkered hard rubber or plastic grips; resembles Browning Model 1906 vest pocket pistol
Estimated Value: $150.00 - $185.00

MAB Model B
Similar to Model A except: top part of slide cut away for empty cartridges to eject at top
Estimated Value: $150.00 - $200.00

MAB Model C
Caliber: 32 ACP, 380 ACP
Action: Semi-automatic; concealed hammer; grip safety & manual safety
Magazine: 7-shot clip in 32 ACP; 6-shot clip in 380 ACP
Barrel: 3¼"
Finish: Blued; checkered hard rubber grips
Estimated Value: $145.00 - $190.00

MAB Model E

MAB Model D
Caliber: 32 ACP, 380 ACP
Action: Semi-automatic; concealed hammer; grip safety & manual safety
Magazine: 9-shot clip in 32 ACP, 8-shot clip in 380 ACP
Barrel: 4"
Finish: Blued; checkered hard rubber grips
Estimated Value: $150.00 - $195.00

MAB Model F
Caliber: 22 long rifle
Action: Semi-automatic; concealed hammer; manual safety; blowback design
Magazine: 9-shot clip
Barrel: 4½", 6", or 7"
Finish: Blued; checkered grips
Estimated Value: $160.00 - $200.00

Semi-automatics

MAB Model E
Caliber: 25 ACP (6.35mm)
Action: Semi-automatic; concealed hammer; manual safety & grip safety
Magazine: 10-shot clip
Barrel: 4"
Finish: Blued; checkered plastic grips; imported into U.S.A. as WAC Model E; importation into U.S.A. discontinued in 1968
Estimated Value: $155.00 - $195.00

MAB Model P-15

MAB Model P-15
Caliber: 9mm Parabellum
Action: Semi-automatic; exposed hammer with round spur; recoil operated with locking breech; manual safety
Magazine: 8-shot clip; 15-shot staggered row clip
Barrel: 4½"
Finish: Blued; checkered grips
Estimated Value: $225.00 - $300.00

MAB Model R
Caliber: 22 long rifle; 32 ACP, 380 ACP, 9mm Parabellum
Action: Semi-automatic; exposed hammer; manual safety
Magazine: 9-shot clip in 22 caliber; 8-shot clip in 32 ACP; 7-shot clip in 380 ACP, 7 or 14-shot clip in 9mm
Barrel: 4½" or 7½" (22); 4" in other calibers
Finish: Blued; checkered grips
Estimated Value: $175.00 - $215.00

Mauser

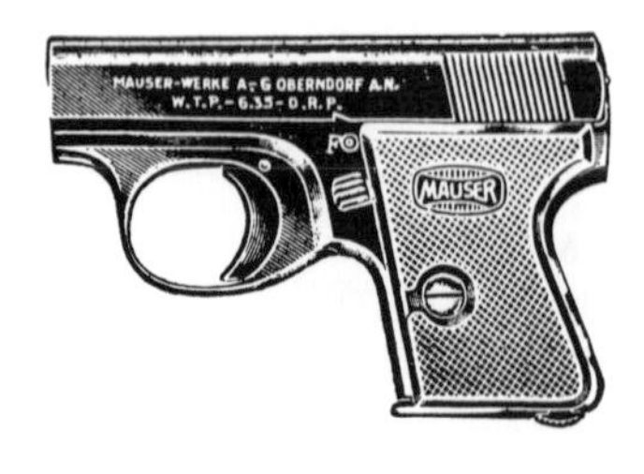

Mauser WTP Model 2 Vest Pocket

Mauser WTP Model 1 Vest Pocket
Caliber: 25 ACP
Action: Semi-automatic; concealed hammer
Magazine: 6-shot clip
Barrel: 2⅜"
Finish: Blued; hard rubber grips
Estimated Value: $225.00 - $300.00

Mauser WTP Model 2 Vest Pocket
Similar to the Model 1 except: curved back strap & trigger guard; smaller size (2" barrel); importation into U.S.A. discontinued in 1968
Estimated Value: $215.00 - $290.00

Mauser Model HSC Pocket Pistol
Caliber: 32 ACP, 380 ACP
Action: Semi-automatic; double action; exposed hammer
Magazine: 8-shot clip
Barrel: 3⅜"
Finish: Blued or nickel; checkered wood grips; add 5% for nickel finish
Estimated Value: $270.00 - $340.00

Mauser Model HSC Pocket Pistol

Mauser Automatic Pocket
Caliber: 25 ACP, 32 ACP
Action: Semi-automatic; concealed hammer
Magazine: 9-shot clip in 25 ACP, 8-shot clip in 32 ACP
Barrel: 3" for 25 ACP; 3½" for 32 ACP
Finish: Blued; checkered walnut or hard rubber grips
Estimated Value: $185.00 - $230.00

Mauser Model 1934 Pocket

Mauser Model 1934 Pocket
Similar to Automatic Pocket Pistol except: larger one-piece wood wrap-around grip; 32 ACP only
Estimated Value: $195.00 - $245.00

Mauser Military Model (Broomhandle Mauser)

Mauser Military Model (Broomhandle Mauser)
Caliber: 7.63 Mauser; 9mm Mauser; 9mm Parabellum (during World War I marked with a large figure "9" cut in the wood grip)
Action: Semi-automatic; exposed hammer; selective fire introduced in 1930 – "N" operated as normal semi-automatic & "R" operated as a machine pistol with fully automatic fire
Magazine: 5 or 10-shot box magazine standard; 5 or 20-shot magazine on selective fire models
Barrel: 5½" standard; also other barrel lengths
Finish: Blued; checkered wood, serrated wood, carved wood, smooth wood, or hard rubber grips; some produced with a shoulder stock holster (wood)
Estimated Value: $1000.00 - $7,500.00

Remington

Remington Model 51
Caliber: 32 ACP, 380 ACP
Action: Semi-automatic; concealed hammer
Magazine: 8-shot clip in 32 ; 7-shot clip in 380
Barrel: 3¼"
Finish: Blued; hard rubber grips
Estimated Value: $300.00 - $375.00

Remington US Model 1911 and 1911 A1
These were pistols made by Remington, on the Colt Patent, for the U.S. Government during World War I & World War II. (See "Colt Government Model 1911 and 1911 A1" for prices.)

Remington Experimental 45 Caliber
An estimated value hasn't been placed on this pistol, since it is not known how many were produced or how they were marked. They were similar to the Remington Model 51 Automatic Pistol except: in 45 caliber, larger, & had an exposed spur hammer. They were made for U.S. Government test purposes about 1917.

Ruger

Ruger Standard Automatic

Ruger Mark II Standard Automatic
Similar to the Standard Automatic except internal improvements; 10-shot clip; slight difference in rear receiver design; 4¾" or 6" round tapered barrel; add 33% for stainless steel
Estimated Value: $140.00 - $175.00

Ruger Standard Automatic
Caliber: 22 long rifle
Action: Semi-automatic; concealed hammer; thumb safety
Magazine: 9-shot clip
Barrel: 4¾" or 6"; tapered round barrel
Finish: Blued; checkered walnut or hard rubber grips; Red eagle insignia on grip used until 1951; add $200.00 for red eagle insignia
Estimated Value: $130.00 - $165.00

Ruger Mark I Target
Similar to Ruger Standard Automatic except: adjustable sights; 6⅞" tapered barrel
Estimated Value: $140.00 - $180.00

Ruger Mark I Bull Barrel Target
Similar to Ruger Mark I Target Pistol except: 5½" untapered heavier barrel
Estimated Value: $145.00 - $185.00

Ruger Mark II Target

Ruger Mark II Target
Similar to the Mark II Standard Automatic except: adjustable sights. 5½", 6⅞, or 10" tapered barrel; add 28% for stainless steel
Estimated Value: $175.00 - $220.00

Ruger Mark I Bull Barrel

Ruger Mark II Bull Barrel Target
Similar to the Mark II Target except; bull barrel; add 28% for stainless steel
Estimated Value: $225.00 - $280.00

Ruger Mark II Government
Similar to the Mark II Bull Barrel except: 6⅞" bull barrel; blued finish only
Estimated Value: $205.00 - $255.00

Important safety warning to owners of Ruger P85 made between 1987 and 1990: If the firing pin is broken, these pistols may fire when the safety/decock lever is depressed. Contact Sturm, Ruger, and Company, Prescott, Arizona 1-(800)-424-1886 to schedule factory modification.

Ruger Model P85
Caliber: 9mm
Action: Double action, recoil operated semi-automatic, ambidextrous safety
Magazine: 15-shot, staggered clip
Barrel: 4½"
Finish: Blued or stainless steel; grooved plastic grips with Ruger insignia; add 12% for stainless steel
Estimated Value: $225.00 - $280.00

Ruger Model P85 Mk II
Same as the Model P85 except: new features and refinements, such as changes to the safety mechanism to prevent firing during decocking, even in the event of a broken firing pin; add 10% for stainless steel
Estimated Value: $245.00 - $310.00

Semi-automatics

Ruger Model P91
Similar to the Model P85 MK II except: 40 S&W; 11-shot clip; stainless steel only; no external safety; available in double action only
Estimated Value: $295.00 - $365.00

Ruger Model P89
Similar to the Model P85 MK II except: decocking lever; also available in double action only; add 10% for stainless steel
Estimated Value: $245.00 - $310.00

Ruger Model P90
Similar to the Model P85 MK II except: 45ACP; 7-shot clip; stainless steel only
Estimated Value: $295.00 - $365.00

Sauer

Sauer 1913 (Old Model)

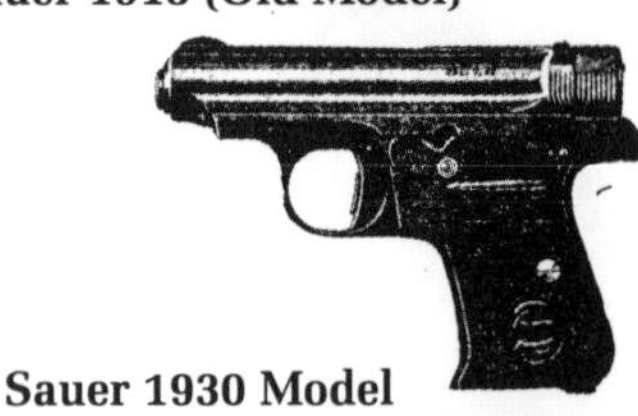

Sauer 1930 Model

Sauer WTM Pocket

Sauer 1913 (Old Model)
Caliber: 32 ACP (7.65mm); 25 ACP (6.35mm)
Action: Semi-automatic; concealed hammer
Magazine: 7-shot clip
Barrel: 3"
Finish: Blued; checkered hard rubber grips
Estimated Value: $200.00 - $250.00

Sauer 1930 Model
Similar to Sauer 1913 (Old Model) except: improved grip design; some models made with indicator pins to show when they were cocked; some models made with alloy slide & receiver
Estimated Value: $210.00 - $265.00

Sauer 1928 Model Pocket
Similar to Sauer WTM Pocket Pistol except: smaller; 2" barrel
Estimated Value: $200.00 - $250.00

Sauer WTM Pocket
Caliber: 25 ACP (6.35mm)
Action: Semi-automatic; concealed hammer
Magazine: 6-shot clip
Barrel: 2⅛"
Finish: Blued; checkered hard rubber grips; fluted slide with top ejection port
Estimated Value: $195.00 - $240.00

Sauer 1938 Model (Model H)
Caliber: 32 ACP (7.65mm)
Action: Semi-automatic; double action; concealed hammer; lever on left side permits hammer to be cocked or uncocked with the thumb
Magazine: 7-shot clip
Barrel: 3¼"
Finish: Blued; checkered plastic grips; some models made with alloy slide; war time models (WWII) inferior to earlier models
Estimated Value:
Pre-war models: $240.00 - $300.00
War models: $175.00 - $220.00

Sauer 1938 Model (Model H)

Savage

Savage Model 1905 Military Type
Caliber: 45 ACP
Action: Semi-automatic; blowback design, grip safety; exposed cocking lever
Magazine: 8-shot clip
Barrel: 5¼"
Finish: Blued, checkered walnut grips; produced for U.S. Government Ordinance Dept. but lost tests to competition
Estimated Value: $1,500.00 - $2,000.00

Savage Model 1907

Savage Model 1907
Caliber: 32 ACP, 380 ACP
Action: Semi-automatic; exposed rounded or spur cocking lever
Magazine: 10-shot in 32 caliber, 9-shot in 380 caliber
Barrel: 3¾" in 32 caliber; 9-shot in 380 caliber
Finish: Blued, metal, hard rubber or wood grips; some military models had lanyard loop
Estimated Value: $190.00 - $250.00

Semi-automatics

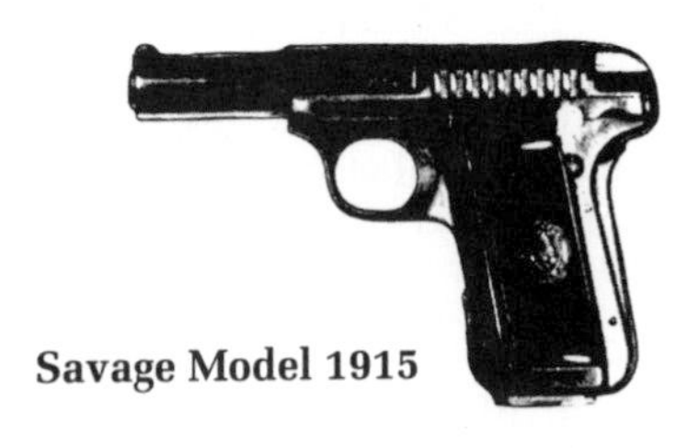
Savage Model 1915

Savage Model 1915
Caliber: 32 ACP, 380 ACP
Action: Semi-automatic; concealed hammer
Magazine: 10-shot in 32 caliber, 9-shot in 380 caliber
Barrel: 3¾" (caliber); 4¼" (380 caliber)
Finish: Blued; hard rubber grips
Estimated Value: $200.00 - $250.00

Savage Model 1917

Savage Model 1917
Caliber: 32 ACP, 380 ACP
Action: Semi-automatic; exposed spur cocking lever; thumb safety
Magazine: 10-shot clip in 32; 9-shot clip in 380, wider magazine than previous models to allow for cartridges to be staggered in a double row
Barrel: 3¾" in 32; 7" in 380
Finish: Blued; hard rubber grips; wide frame & flared grips
Estimated Value: $220.00 - $275.00

Smith & Wesson

Smith & Wesson Model 32 Automatic

Smith & Wesson
Model 32 Automatic
Caliber: 32 ACP
Action: Semi-automatic; concealed hammer; grip safety located on front of grip below trigger guard
Magazine: 7-shot clip
Barrel: 3½"; barrel is fixed to the frame; the slide fits into guides on the barrel
Finish: Blued; smooth walnut grips
Estimated Value: $800.00 - $1,000.00

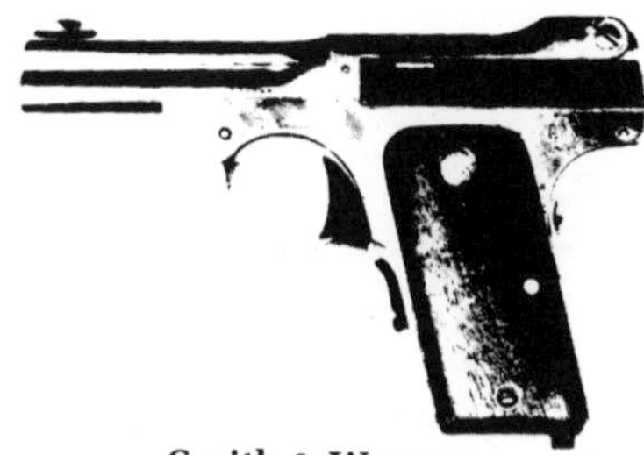

Smith & Wesson Model 35 Automatic

Smith & Wesson Model 35 Automatic
Caliber: 35 S&W automatic
Action: Semi-automatic; concealed hammer; grip safety located on front of grip below trigger guard; manual safety at rear of left grip
Magazine: 7-shot clip
Barrel: 3½"; barrel hinged to rear of frame
Finish: Blued or nickel; smooth walnut grips
Estimated Value: $520.00 - $650.00

Smith & Wesson Model 39
Caliber: 9mm (Parabellum) Luger
Action: Semi-automatic; double action; exposed hammer; thumb safety
Magazine: 8-shot clip
Barrel: 4"
Finish: Blued or nickel; checkered walnut grips; pistol has aluminum alloy frame except approximately 925 pistols were produced with steel frames; add $25.00 for nickel finish
Estimated Value:
Alloy frame: $275.00 - $350.00
Steel Frame: $850.00 - $1,050.00

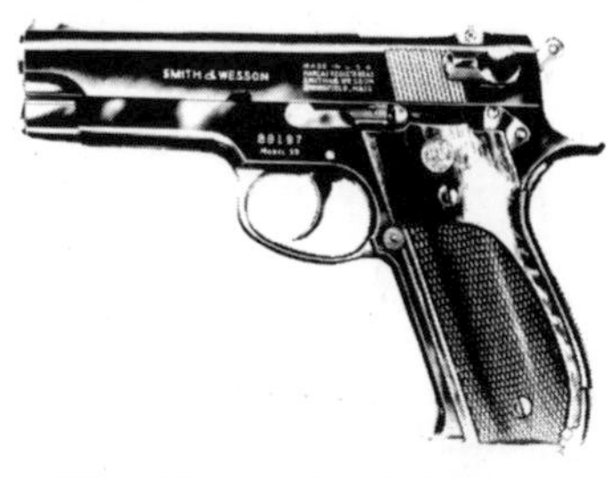

Smith & Wesson Model 39

Smith & Wesson Model 59 Double Action

Smith & Wesson Model 59
Caliber: 9mm (Parabellum) Luger
Action: Semi-automatic; double action; exposed hammer; thumb safety
Magazine: 14-shot staggered column clip
Barrel: 4"
Finish: Blued or nickel; checkered high impact molded nylon grip; add $28.00 for nickel finish
Estimated Value: $250.00 - $325.00

Semi-automatics

Smith & Wesson Model 41

Caliber: 22 short or 22 long rifle (not interchangeable)
Action: Single action; semi-automatic; concealed hammer; thumb safety
Magazine: 10-shot clip
Barrel: 5½" heavy barrel or 7" regular barrel
Finish: Blued; checkered walnut grips with thumb rest
Estimated Value: $445.00 - $550.00

Smith & Wesson Model 41

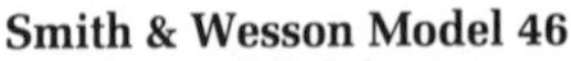

Smith & Wesson Model 46

Similar to Model 41 except: 22 long rifle caliber only; plastic grips with thumb rest
Estimated Value: $385.00 - $480.00

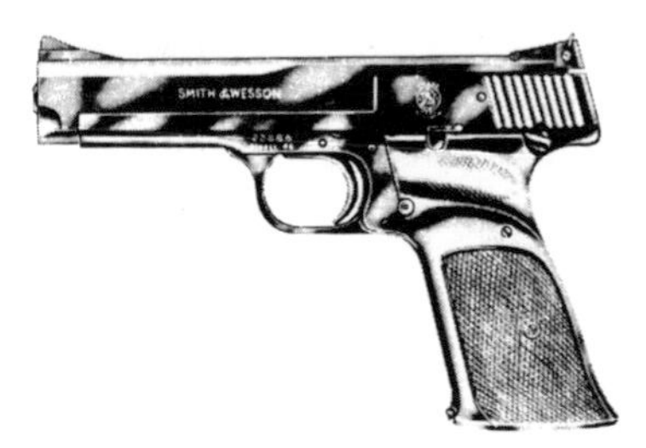

Smith & Wesson Model 46

Smith & Wesson Model 52, 38 Master

Caliber: 38 Special (mid-range wadcutter only)
Action: Single action; semi-automatic; exposed hammer; thumb safety
Magazine: 5-shot clip
Barrel: 5"
Finish: Blued; checkered walnut grips
Estimated Value: $535.00 - $665.00

Smith & Wesson Model 52

Smith & Wesson Model 61 Escort

Caliber: 22 long rifle
Action: Semi-automatic; concealed hammer; thumb safety
Magazine: 5-shot clip
Barrel: 2⅛"
Finish: Blued or nickel; checkered plastic grips; add $15.00 for nickel finish
Estimated Value: $205.00 - $260.00

Smith & Wesson Model 439

Smith & Wesson Model 439
Caliber: 9mm (Parabellum) Luger
Action: Semi-automatic; double action; exposed hammer; thumb safety
Magazine: 8-shot clip
Barrel: 4"
Finish: Blued or nickel; checkered walnut grips; frame is constructed of aluminum alloy; add 8% for nickel finish
Estimated Value: $285.00 - $355.00

Smith & Wesson Model 539
Similar to the Model 439 except: frame is constructed of steel; add 8% for nickel finish
Estimated Value: $280.00 - $350.00

Smith & Wesson Model 639
Similar to the Model 439 except; satin stainless steel finish; add 4% for adjustable rear sight
Estimated Value: $315.00 - $395.00

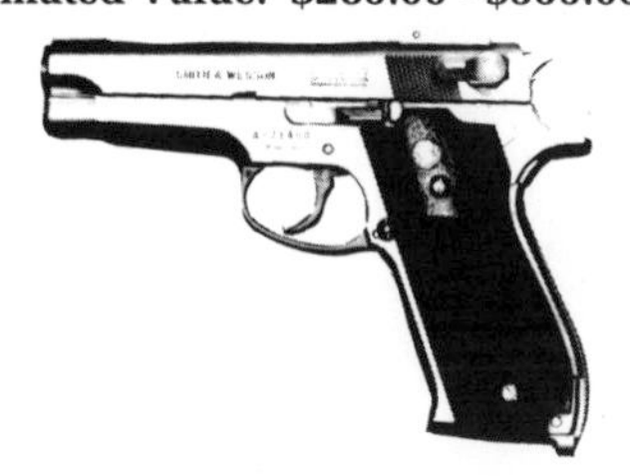

Smith & Wesson Model 639

Smith & Wesson Model 459
Caliber: 9mm (Parabellum) Luger
Action: Semi-automatic; double action
Magazine: 14-shot staggered clip
Barrel: 4"
Finish: Blued or nickel; checkered high-impact molded nylon grips; frame is constructed of aluminum alloy; straight back strap; the grip is thick to accommodate the staggered column magazine; add 8% for nickel finish
Estimated Value: $300.00 - $375.00

Smith & Wesson Model 459

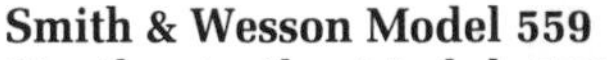

Smith & Wesson Model 559
Similar to the Model 459 except: steel frame; add 8% for nickel finish
Estimated Value: $290.00 - $365.00

Smith & Wesson Model 659
Similar to the Model 459 except: satin stainless steel finish; add 4% for adjustable rear sight
Estimated Value: $330.00 - $415.00

Smith & Wesson Model 659

Semi-automatics

Smith & Wesson Model 645

Smith & Wesson Model 645
Caliber: 45 ACP
Action: Double action; semi-automatic; exposed hammer
Magazine: 8-shot clip
Barrel: 5"
Finish: Stainless steel; checkered high-impact molded nylon grips
Estimated Value: $370.00 - $465.00

Smith & Wesson Model 422

Smith & Wesson Model 745
Caliber: 45ACP
Action: Single action; semi-automatic; adjustable trigger stop
Magazine: 8-shot clip
Barrel: 5"
Finish: Stainless steel frame; blued carbon steel slide, hammer, trigger, sights; checkered walnut grips
Estimated Value: $440.00 - $550.00

Smith & Wesson Model 622

Smith & Wesson Model 422
Caliber: 22 long rifle
Action: Single action; semi-automatic; concealed hammer
Magazine: 12-shot clip
Barrel: 4½" or 6" barrel
Finish: Blued; aluminum frame, carbon steel slide; plastic grips on field model, checkered walnut on target model; add 25% for target model
Estimated Value: $130.00 - $160.00

Smith & Wesson Model 2206
Same as the Model 422 except: stainless steel slide & frame; add 4% for adjustable target sights
Estimated Value: $180.00 - $225.00

Smith & Wesson Model 622
Same as the Model 422 except stainless steel slide & aluminum alloy frame; add 20% for target sights
Estimated Value: $155.00 - $195.00

Smith & Wesson Model 469

Smith & Wesson Model 469
Caliber: 9mm (Parabellum) Luger
Action: Double action; semi-automatic; exposed bobbed hammer
Magazine: 12-shot clip
Barrel: 3½"
Finish: Blued; pebble grain molded Debrin grips; aluminum alloy frame
Estimated Value: $290.00 - $360.00

Smith & Wesson Model 669
Same as the model 469 except: barrel & slide are stainless steel
Estimated Value: $310.00 - $390.00

Smith & Wesson Model 1006
Caliber: 10mm
Action: Double action; semi-automatic, exposed hammer, ambidextrous safety
Magazine: 9-shot clip
Barrel: 5"
Finish: Stainless steel, Debrin one-piece wrap-around grip with straight back strap; add 4% for adjustable rear sight
Estimated Value: $450.00 - $560.00

Smith & Wesson Model 1006

Smith & Wesson Model 3904
Caliber: 9mm
Action: Double action, semi-automatic with exposed hammer & ambidextrous safety
Magazine: 8-shot clip
Barrel: 4"
Finish: Blued; aluminum alloy frame, carbon steel slide; Debrin one-piece wrap-around grips with curved back strap; add 5% for adjustable rear sight
Estimated Value: $310.00 - $390.00

Smith & Wesson Model 3906
Same as the Model 3904 except: stainless steel; add 5% for adjustable rear sight
Estimated Value: $350.00 - $440.00

Smith & Wesson Model 5903
Caliber: 9mm Luger Parabellum
Action: Double action, semi-automatic, ambidextrous safety, exposed hammer
Magazine: 15-shot clip
Barrel: 4"
Finish: Stainless steel slide with aluminum alloy frame; Debrin one-piece wrap-around grip with curved back strap; add 5% for adjustable rear sight
Estimated Value: $395.00 - $490.00

Smith & Wesson Model 5903

Smith & Wesson Model 5904
Same as the Model 5903 except blued finish with carbon steel slide; add 5% for adjustable rear sight
Estimated Value: $365.00 - $460.00

Smith & Wesson Model 5906
Same as the Model 5903 except: stainless steel slide & frame; add 5% for adjustable rear sight; add 15% for fixed night sights
Estimated Value: $400.00 - $505.00

Smith & Wesson Model 5906

Smith & Wesson Model 5926
Similar to the Model 5903 except: fixed sights only; stainless steel slide and frame; no manual safety; it uses a decocking lever to lower the hammer from the cocked position (this permits the pistol to be fired double action without moving a safety
Estimated Value: $420.00 - $520.00

Smith & Wesson Model 5946
Same as the Model 5926 except: no decocking lever; it can only be fired double action for each shot; bobbed hammer
Estimated Value: $405.00 - $500.00

Smith & Wesson
Model 3913 (Lady Smith)

Smith & Wesson Model 3913 (Lady Smith)
Caliber: 9mm Luger Parabellum
Action: Double action, semi-automatic with bobbed hammer & ambidextrous safety
Magazine: 8-shot clip
Barrel: 3½"
Finish: Stainless steel slide; black Debrin one-piece wrap-around grip; small, compact double action 9mm automatic specially designed for the female shooter
Estimated Value: $325.00 - $405.00

Smith & Wesson Model 3914

Smith & Wesson Model 3914
Same as the Model 3913 except: blued finish carbon steel slide and alloy frame with gray Debrin one-piece wrap-around grip
Estimated Value: $425.00 - $530.00

Smith & Wesson Models 3953 & 3954
Same as the Models 3913 and 3914 except: double action only; no safety lever; Model 3953 has stainless steel slide and alloy frame; model 3954 has blued finish with carbon steel slide and alloy frame; add 11% for stainless steel slide (Model 3953)
Estimated Value: $315.00 - $395.00

Smith & Wesson Model 6904
Caliber: 9mm Luger Parabellum
Action: Double action, semi-automatic; exposed bobbed hammer; ambidextrous safety
Magazine: 12-shot clip
Barrel: 3½"
Finish: Blued, carbon steel slide with aluminum alloy frame; Debrin one-piece wrap-around grip with curved backstrap
Estimated Value: $345.00 - $430.00

Smith & Wesson Model 6906
Same as the Model 6904 except: stainless steel slide with aluminum alloy frame; add 16% for night sights
Estimated Value: $380.00 - $475.00

Smith & Wesson Model 6906

Semi-automatics

Smith & Wesson Model 2213

Smith & Wesson Model 6946
Same as the Model 6906 except: double action only for each shot; no safety lever
Estimated Value: $380.00 - $475.00

Smith & Wesson Model 1066
Similar to the Model 6906 except: 4¼" barrel; fixed sights
Estimated Value: $440.00 - $550.00

Smith & Wesson Model 1076
Same as the Model 1066 except: decocking lever; no manual safety
Estimated Value: $450.00 - $565.00

Smith & Wesson Model 1086
Same as the Model 1066 except: double action only; bobbed hammer; no decocking lever; no manual safety
Estimated Value: $440.00 - $550.00

Smith & Wesson Model 2214

Smith & Wesson Model 2213 & 2214
Caliber: 22 long rifle
Action: Single action, semi-automatic; concealed hammer
Magazine: 8-shot clip
Barrel: 3"
Finish: Model 2213 has stainless steel slide with alloy frame. Model 2214 is blued carbon steel slide with alloy frame
Estimated Value: $360.00 - $450.00

Smith & Wesson Model 4006

Smith & Wesson Model 4006
Caliber: 40 S&W
Action: Double action, semi-automatic; exposed hammer; ambidextrous safety
Magazine: 11-shot clip
Barrel: 4"
Finish: Stainless steel slide and frame; Debrin one-piece wrap-around straight backstrap grip; add 4% for adjustable sights; add 15% for fixed night sights
Estimated Value: $425.00 - $530.00

Smith & Wesson Model 4046
Same as the Model 4006 except: double action only for each shot; no manual safety; bobbed hammer; add 15% for fixed night sights
Estimated Value: $425.00 - $530.00

Smith & Wesson Model 4026
Same as the Model 4006 except: it has a decocking lever to lower the hammer; no manual safety
Estimated Value: $435.00 - $540.00

Smith & Wesson Model 4026

Smith & Wesson Model 4053 & 4054
Same as Models 4043 and 4044 except: more compact; 3½" barrel; add 9% for stainless steel slide
Estimated Value: $375.00 - $470.00

Smith & Wesson Model 4013 & 4014
Same as the Model 4003 & 4004 except: more compact; 3½" barrel; Model 4013 has stainless steel slide and alloy frame; Model 4014 has blue finish with carbon steel slide and alloy frame; add 9% for stainless steel slide (4013)
Estimated Value: $375.00 - $470.00

Smith & Wesson Model 4046

**Smith & Wesson
Models 4003 & 4004**
Same as the Model 4006 except: Model 4003 has aluminum alloy frame and stainless steel slide; Model 4004 has aluminum alloy frame and carbon steel slide with blued finish; add 7% for stainless steel slide model (4003)
Estimated Value: $385.00 - $480.00

**Smith & Wesson
Models 4043 & 4044**
Same as the Models 4003 and 4004 except: double action only with bobbed hammer; no manual safety; add 7% for stainless steel slide model (4043)
Estimated Value: $385.00 - $480.00

Smith & Wesson Model 4043

Semi-automatics

Smith & Wesson Model 4506
Caliber: 45ACP
Action: Double action, semi-automatic; exposed hammer, ambidextrous safety
Magazine: 8-shot clip
Barrel: 5"
Finish: Stainless steel frame and slide with Debrin one-piece wrap-around grip; add 4% for adjustable rear sight
Estimated Value: $440.00 - $550.00

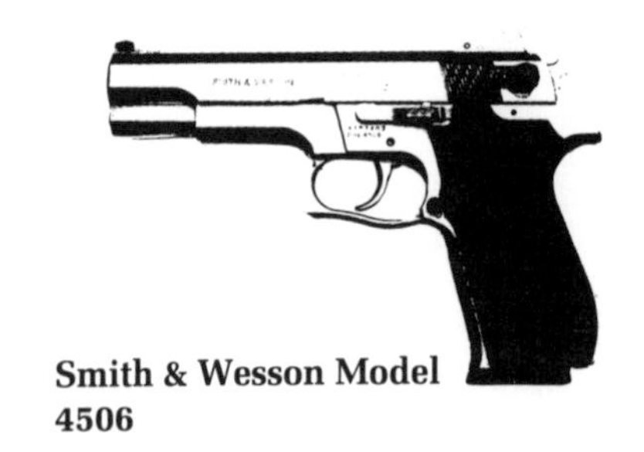

Smith & Wesson Model 4506

Smith & Wesson Model 4566
Same as the Model 4506 except: 4¼" barrel; more compact
Estimated Value: $440.00 - $550.00

Smith & Wesson Model 4566

Smith & Wesson Model 4576
Same as the Model 4506 except: more compact; 4¼" barrel; decocking lever; no manual safety
Estimated Value: $455.00 - $570.00

Smith & Wesson Model 4586
Same as the Model 4576 except: double action only; no decocking lever; no manual safety
Estimated Value: $440.00 - $550.00

Smith & Wesson Model 4516
Caliber: 45ACP
Action: Double action, semi-automatic, exposed hammer; ambidextrous safety
Magazine: 7-shot clip
Barrel: 3¾"
Finish: Stainless steel frame and slide with Debrin one-piece wrap around grip
Estimated Value: $440.00 - $550.00

Smith & Wesson Model 4516

Star

Star Model 1919 Pocket

Star Model 1919 Pocket
Caliber: 25 ACP (6.35mm)
Action: Semi-automatic; exposed hammer; safety on top rear of the slide
Magazine: 8-shot clip
Barrel: 2⅝"
Finish: Blued; checkered walnut grips
Estimated Value: $180.00 - $225.00

Star Model CO Pocket

Star Model CO Pocket
Improved version of the 1919 Model; safety in front of left grip rather than top of slide; plastic grips; some engraved nickel plated models produced; add $20.00 for engraved nickel model
Estimated Value: $160.00 - $200.00

Star Model H
Similar to Model CO pistol except: caliber 32 ACP; 9-shot clip
Estimated Value: $130.00 - $165.00

Star Model HN
Same as Model H except: caliber 380 ACP; 6-shot clip
Estimated Value: $140.00 - $175.00

Star Model H

Semi-automatics

Star Model E Pocket
Caliber: 25 ACP (6.35mm)
Action: Semi-automatic; exposed hammer; safety located in front of left grip
Magazine: 6-shot clip
Barrel: 2"
Finish: Blued; checkered grips
Estimated Value: $145.00 - $180.00

Star Model A & AS
Caliber: 9mm Luger, 9mm Bergman, 9mm Largo, 38 Super auto
Action: Semi-automatic; exposed hammer
Magazine: 8-shot clip
Barrel: 5"
Finish: Blued; checkered walnut grips; resembles the 1911 A1 Colt
Estimated Value: $160.00 - $200.00

Star Model B
Similar to Model A except: barrel lengths 4¼" or 6½"; caliber 9mm Parabellum only
Estimated Value: $175.00 - $220.00

Star Model B Super

Star Model F & FR

Star Model B Super
Caliber: 9mm Parabellum
Action: Semi-automatic; exposed hammer; loaded chamber indicator;
Magazine: 8-shot clip
Barrel: 5"
Finish: Blued or nickel; add 9% for nickel finish
Estimated Value: $200.00 - $250.00

Star Model F & FR
Caliber: 22 long rifle
Action: Semi-automatic; exposed hammer; manual safety at top rear of left grip
Magazine: 10-shot clip
Barrel: 4¼" (regular); 6" & 7" on Sport & Target models
Finish: Blued, chromed or chromed engraved; plastic grips; add 10% for chrome; add 25% for chrome engraved model
Estimated Value: $125.00 - $160.00

Star Model M (Military)

Star Model I (Police Model)
Caliber: 32 ACP
Action: Semi-automatic; exposed hammer
Magazine: 9-shot clip
Barrel: 4¾"
Finish: Blued; plastic grips
Estimated Value: $120.00 - $150.00

Star Model IN
Same as Model I except: caliber 380 ACP; 8-shot clip
Estimated Value: $130.00 - $160.00

Star Model M (Military)
Caliber: 380 ACP; 9mm Luger; 9mm Bergmann, 38 ACP, 45 ACP
Action: Semi-automatic; exposed hammer; manual safety
Magazine: 7-shot clip in 45 caliber, 8-shot clip in all other calibers
Barrel: 5"
Finish: Blued; checkered grips; a modified version of the U.S. Government Colt 1911 45 automatic
Estimated Value: $150.00 - $200.00

Star Model Super Star

Star Model Super Star
Same as Model M except: 38 Super ACP, 9mm Parabellum & 38 ACP only; addition of disarming bolt; improved sights; magazine safety
Estimated Value: $180.00 - $225.00

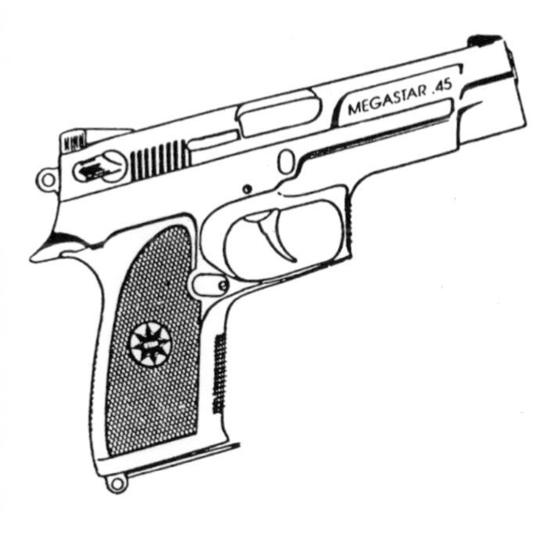

Star Megastar

Star Megastar
Caliber: 10 mm, 45 ACP
Action: Double action, semi-automatic; exposed hammer; ambidextrous safety
Magazine: 12-shot clip
Barrel: 4½"
Finish: All-steel blued or all-weather Starvel finish; rubber grips; add 5% for Starvel finish
Estimated Value: $395.00 - $495.00

Semi-automatics

Star Firestar, M43
Caliber: 9mm Parabellum, 40 S&W, 45 ACP; add 5% for 40 caliber; add 12% for 45 caliber
Action: Double action, semi-automatic; exposed hammer; ambidextrous safety
Magazine: 7-shot clip, 6-shot in 40 or 45 caliber
Barrel: 3½"
Finish: All-steel blued or all-weather Starvel finish; add 7% for Starvel finish
Estimated Value: $260.00 - $325.00

Star Firestar

Star Model 31P & 31PK

Star Model 31P & 31PK
Caliber: 9mm Parabellum, 40 S&W; add 11% for 40 S&W
Action: Double action, semi-automatic; exposed hammer; ambidextrous safety & decocking lever
Magazine: 15-shot clip
Barrel: 3¾"
Finish: 31P has all-steel construction in blued or Starvel finish; add 6% for all-weather Starvel finish; 31PK has alloy frame in blued finish only
Estimated Value: $330.00 - $410.00

Star Model DK (Starfire)
Caliber: 380 ACP
Action: Semi-automatic; exposed hammer; manual safety at top rear of left grip
Magazine: 6-shot clip
Barrel: 5"
Finish: Blued; checkered plastic grips
Estimated Value: $175.00 - $220.00

Star Model S
Caliber: 38 ACP
Action: Semi-automatic; exposed hammer; manual safety
Magazine: 7-shot clip
Barrel: 4"
Finish: Blued or chromed; engraved; plastic grips
Estimated Value: $160.00 - $200.00

Star Model SI
Same as Model S except: caliber 32 ACP; 8-shot clip
Estimated Value: $150.00 - $190.00

Star Model Super S
Same as Model S except: disarming bolt; magazine safety
Estimated Value: $180.00 - $225.00

Star Model Super SI
Same as Model Super S except: caliber 32 ACP; 8-shot clip
Estimated Value: $160.00 - $200.00

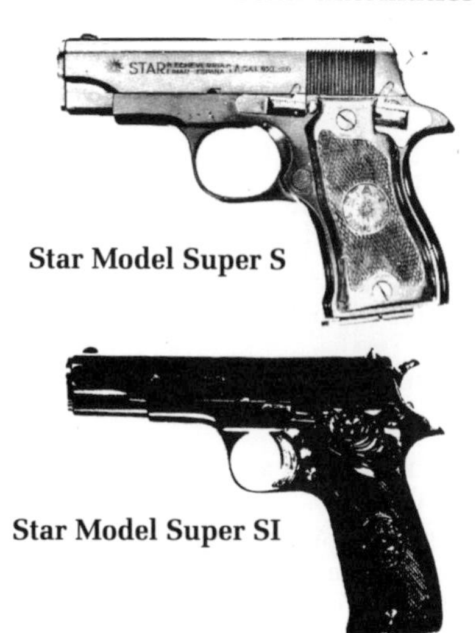

Star Model Super S

Star Model Super SI

Star Model CU (Starlet)
Caliber: 25 ACP
Action: Semi-automatic; exposed hammer
Magazine: 8-shot clip
Barrel: 2⅜"
Finish: Blued or chromed slide; black, gray, gold, blue, or green receiver; checkered plastic grips; alloy frame
Estimated Value: $150.00 - $190.00

Star Model HF (Lancer)

Star Model HF (Lancer)
Basically same as Model CU Starlet except: caliber 22 long rifle; 3" barrel
Estimated Value: $145.00 - $180.00

Star Model Super SM
Caliber: 380 ACP
Action: Semi-automatic; exposed hammer
Magazine: 9-shot clip
Barrel: 4"
Finish: Blued or chrome; checkered wood grips; add 4% for chrome model
Estimated Value: $190.00 - $240.00

Star Model Super SM

Semi-automatics

Star Model 28

Star Model 28
Caliber: 9mm Parabellum
Action: Semi-automatic; double action; exposed hammer
Magazine: 15-shot clip
Barrel: 4¼"
Finish: Blued; checkered plastic grips
Estimated Value: $240.00 - $315.00

Star Model 30PK
An improved version of the Model 28 with alloy frame & slightly shorter length; combat-style trigger guard
Estimated Value: $305.00 - $380.00

Star Model 30 M
Similar to the Model 30PK except steel frame
Estimated Value: $320.00 - $400.00

Star Model BKM

Star Model BKS

Star Model BKS, BKM
Caliber: 9mm Parabellum
Action: Semi-automatic; exposed hammer; manual thumb safety
Magazine: 8-shot clip
Barrel: 4½"
Finish: Blued or chrome; add 4% for chrome; checkered walnut grips; alloy frame
Estimated Value: $235.00 - $295.00

Star Model BM

Star Model BM
Similar to the Model BKM except: steel frame; add $15.00 for chrome finish; add 13% for Starvel weather resistant finish
Estimated Value: $225.00 - $280.00

Star Model PD

Star Model PD
Caliber: 45 ACP
Action: Semi-automatic; exposed hammer
Magazine: 6-shot clip
Barrel: 4"
Finish: Blued, chrome, or Starvel weather resistant finish; add 3% for chrome; add 10% for Starvel finish; checkered wood grips
Estimated Value: $270.00 - $340.00

Sterling

Sterling Model 283
Caliber: 22 long rifle
Action: Semi-automatic; exposed hammer; adjustable trigger & a rear lock safety
Magazine: 10-shot clip
Barrel: 4½", 6" or 8" heavy bull barrel
Finish: Blued; checkered plastic grips; all steel construction
Estimated Value: $120.00 - $150.00

Sterling Model 283

Sterling Model 284
Same as Model 283 automatic pistol except: lighter tapered barrel, also know as Target 300L Model
Estimated Value: $125.00 - $150.00

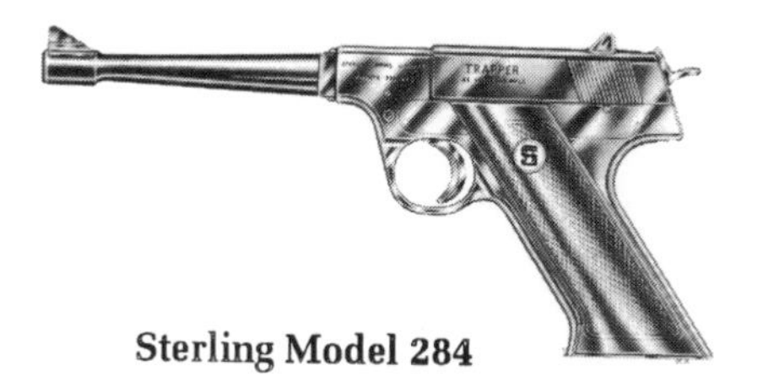
Sterling Model 284

Sterling Model 285
Same as Model 283 automatic pistol except: 4½" heavy barrel only; non-adjustable trigger; also known as Husky Model
Estimated Value: $125.00 - $160.00

Semi-automatics

Sterling Model 286

Sterling Model 286
Same as Model 283 automatic pistol except: 4½" & 6" tapered barrel only; non-adjustable trigger, also known as Trapper Model
Estimated Value: $110.00 - $140.00

Sterling Model MKII 400

Sterling Model 400 Automatic Pistol
Caliber: 380 ACP
Action: Semi-automatic; double action; exposed hammer; safety locks firing pin
Magazine: 6-shot clip
Barrel: 3½"
Finish: Blued or nickel; add 10% for nickel; checkered grips
Estimated Value: $150.00 - $190.00

Sterling MK II 400 & MK II400S
Similar to 400 except: streamlined & lightweight; also 32 ACP; add 5% for nickel finish; add 15% for stainless steel (MK II 400S)
Estimated Value: $145.00 - $180.00

Sterling Model 400S
Similar to Model 400 except: stainless steel
Estimated Value: $170.00 - $220.00

Sterling Model 402
Similar to Model 400 except: 22 long rifle; 8-shot clip; add $10.00 for nickel finish
Estimated Value: $135.00 - $175.00

Sterling Model MK II 402, MK II 402S
Similar to the Model 400 MK II except: 32 ACP caliber; Model 402S MK II is stainless steel; add 15% for stainless steel
Estimated Value: $160.00 - $200.00

Sterling Model 402

Sterling Model 300

Sterling Model 300, 300S
Caliber: 25 ACP
Action: Semi-automatic blowback action; concealed hammer
Magazine: 6-shot clip
Barrel: 2½"
Finish: Blued, nickel or stainless steel; add 10% for nickel; add 20% for stainless steel
Estimated Value: $65.00 - $90.00

Sterling Model 302

Sterling Model 302, 302S
Same as Model 300 Automatic Pistol except: 22 long rifle; model 302S is stainless steel; add 20% for stainless steel
Estimated Value: $90.00 - $110.00

Steyr

Roth-Steyr Self-Loading Pistol
Caliber: 8mm Roth-Steyr
Action: Semi-automatic concealed striker; locked breech design uses rotation of barrel by cam action to unlock barrel when fired; the striker is cocked by the recoil, but the trigger action has to pull it further back before it will release to fire; one of the earliest forms of successful locked-breech pistols
Magazine: 10-shot non-detachable; loaded from the top
Barrel: 5⅛"
Finish: Blued; checkered wood grips
Estimated Value: $140.00 - $175.00

Roth-Steyr Self-Loading Pistol

Steyr Model 1909
Pocket Automatic Pistol
Caliber: 32 ACP
Action: Semi-automatic; concealed hammer; blowback action; early models have no extractor (empty case is blown out by gas after the breech-block is pushed open by firing); barrel can be tipped down for cleaning, using as single shot pistol, or removing unfired cartridge
Magazine: 7-shot clip
Barrel: 3½"
Finish: Blued; checkered wood grips; add $20.00 for later model with extractor
Estimated Value: $160.00 - $200.00

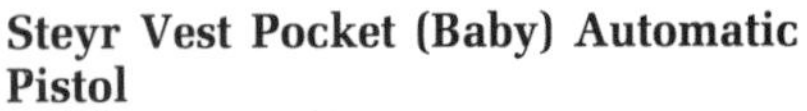

Steyr Vest Pocket (Baby) Automatic Pistol
Caliber: 25 ACP
Action: Semi-automatic; concealed hammer; blowback action; early models have no extractor (empty case is blown out by gas); barrel can be tipped down for cleaning, using as a single shot pistol, or for removing unfired cartridges
Magazine: 6-shot clip
Barrel: 2"
Finish: Blued; hard rubber checkered grips; add $20.00 for later model with extractor
Estimated Value: $140.00 - $175.00

Steyr Vest Pocket (Baby) Automatic

Steyr Model 1912 Military

Steyr Model 1912 Military
Caliber: 9mm Steyr
Action: Semi-automatic; exposed hammer; short recoil; locked breech action (barrel rotates to unlock breech when gun is fired)
Magazine: 8-shot non-detachable; loaded from top singly or by using a strip clip
Barrel: 5"
Finish: Blued; checkered wood grips; adopted by the Austro-Hungarian Army in 1912
Estimated Value: $240.00 - $300.00

Steyr Nazi-Proofed
Same as Steyr Model 1912 except: converted to fire the 9mm Luger cartridge during World War II & marked "P-08" on left side of slide
Estimated Value: $260.00 - $325.00

Steyr-Solothurn Pocket Model Automatic Pistol
Similar to the Steyr model 1909 except: a modified version; has extractors to remove empties
Estimated Value: $170.00 - $210.00

Steyr Model GB
Caliber: 9mm Parabellum
Action: Gas (delayed) blowback action, semi-automatic, double action
Magazine: 18-shot clip
Barrel: 5½"
Finish: Black crinkled with blued slide; plastic checkered grips
Estimated Value: $335.00 - $445.00

Taurus

Taurus Model 58, PT58
Caliber: 380 ACP
Action: Semi-automatic, double action; exposed round spur hammer
Magazine: 13-shot staggered clip
Barrel: 4"
Finish: Blued, satin nickel, or stainless steel; add 5% for satin nickel finish; add 13% for stainless steel; smooth walnut grips
Estimated Value: $253.00 - $315.00

Taurus Model PT58

Taurus Model PT92AF, PT99AF
Caliber: 9mm Parabellum
Action: Semi-automatic, double action; exposed round spur hammer
Magazine: 15-shot clip
Barrel: 5"
Finish: Blued, satin nickel or stainless steel; add 8% for satin nickel finish; add 15% for stainless steel; smooth walnut grips; add 8% for PT99AF (adj. rear sight)
Estimated Value: $285.00 - $355.00

Taurus Model PT92AF

Taurus Model 92 AFC
A compact version of the Model 92AF with 4" barrel & 13-shot clip; add 8% for nickel finish
Estimated Value: $285.00 - $355.00

Semi-automatics

Taurus Model PT-22, PT-25
Caliber: 22 long rifle (PT-22); 25ACP (PT-25)
Action: Double action only; semi-automatic; tip-up barrel
Magazine: 9-shot clip (PT-22); 8-shot clip (PT-25)
Barrel: 2¾" tip-up
Finish: Blued; smooth Brazilian hardwood grips; finger rest on clip
Estimated Value: $110.00 - $135.00

Taurus Model PT-22

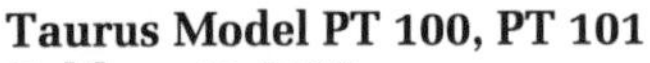

Taurus Model PT 100, PT 101
Caliber: 40 S&W
Action: Double action only; semi-automatic; ambidextrous safety
Magazine: 11-shot clip
Barrel: 5"
Finish: Blued, satin nickel, or satin stainless steel; add 8% for nickel finish; add 13% for stainless steel; Brazilian hardwood grips; add 8% for PT 101
Estimated Value: $110.00 - $135.00

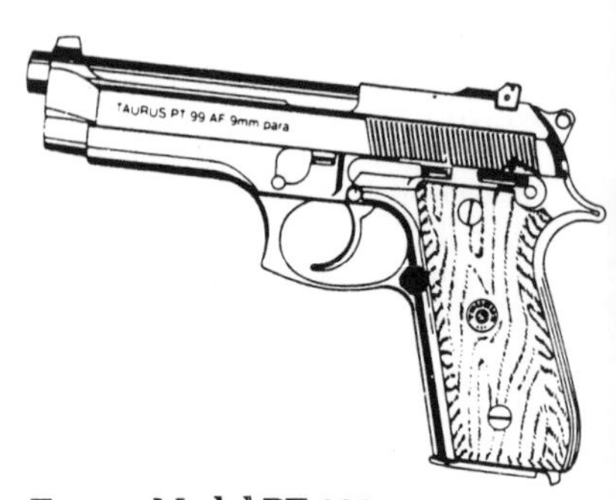

Taurus Model PT 100

Walther

Walther Model 1 Vest Pocket
Caliber: 25 ACP
Action: Semi-automatic; concealed hammer
Magazine: 6-shot clip
Barrel: 2"
Finish: Blued; checkered hard rubber grips; top section of slide is cut away
Estimated Value: $245.00 - $310.00

Walther Model 2 Vest Pocket
Similar to Model 1 except: slide fully encloses the barrel; ejector port right side of slide
Estimated Value: $255.00 - $320.00

Walther Model 3 Pocket
Caliber: 32 ACP
Action: Semi-automatic; concealed hammer
Magazine: 6-shot clip
Barrel: 2⅝"
Finish: Blued; checkered hard rubber grips; ejector port on left side of slide
Estimated Value: $285.00 - $360.00

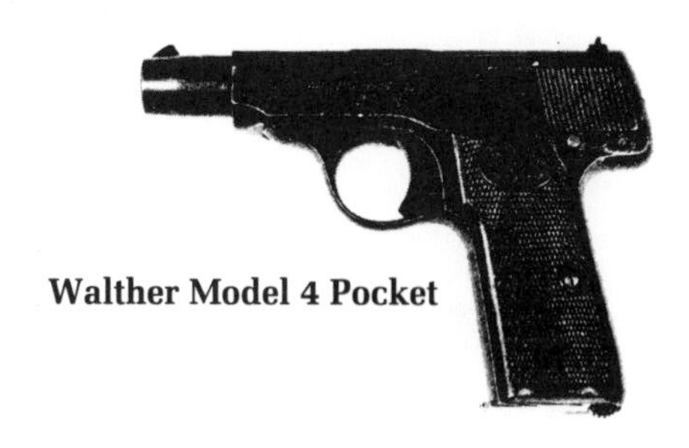

Walther Model 4 Pocket

Walther Model 4 Pocket
Similar to Model 3 except: larger in overall size; 3½" barrel; longer grip; 8-shot clip; a slide extension connected to forward end of the slide
Estimated Value: $320.00 - $400.00

Walther Model 5 Vest Pocket Pistol

Walther Model 5 Vest Pocket Pistol
Similar to Model 2 except: improved version with a better finish
Estimated Value: $265.00 - $330.00

Walther Model 6
Caliber: 9mm Parabellum
Action: Semi-automatic; concealed hammer
Magazine: 8-shot clip
Barrel: 4¾"
Finish: Blued; hard rubber grips
Estimated Value: $400.00 - $500.00

Walther Model 6 Vest Pocket
Caliber: 25 ACP
Action: Semi-automatic; concealed hammer
Magazine: 6-shot clip
Barrel: 2"
Finish: Blued; checkered plastic grips; top section of slide is cut away; also nickel or gold plated engraved finishes with pearl or ivory grips; the Special plated & engraved styles worth more
Estimated Value: $240.00 - $300.00

Walther Model 6 Vest Pocket

Walther Model 7 Pocket

Walther Model 7 Pocket
Caliber: 25 ACP
Action: Semi-automatic; concealed hammer
Magazine: 8-shot clip
Barrel: 3"
Finish: Blued; checkered hard rubber grips
Estimated Value: $285.00 - $360.00

Walther Model 8 Pocket
Caliber: 25 ACP
Action: Semi-automatic; concealed hammer
Magazine: 8-shot clip
Barrel: 2⅞"
Finish: Blued; checkered plastic grips; a variety of special styles were made such as nickel or gold-plated, engraved finishes with pearl or ivory grips; special plated & engraved styles worth more
Estimated Value: $265.00 - $335.00

Walther Model 8 Lightweight Pocket
Same as Model 8 except: aluminum alloy frame
Estimated Value: $270.00 - $340.00

Walther Model PP
Caliber: 22 long rifle, 25 ACP, 32 ACP, or 380 ACP
Action: Semi-automatic; double action; exposed hammer; thumb safety that drops the hammer on blocked firing pin
Magazine: 8-shot clip
Barrel: 3¾"
Finish: Blued; checkered plastic or checkered wood grips; steel back strap; nickel, silver, & gold plated engraved models with ivory & pearl grips; special plated & engraved models worth more
Estimated Value: $300.00 - $460.00

Walther Model PP

Walther Model PPK
Same as Model PP except: 3¼" barrel; 7-shot magazine; one piece wrap-around grip
Estimated Value: $275.00 - $450.00

Walther Models PP & PPK Lightweight
Same as Models PP & PPK except: aluminum alloy frame
Estimated Value: $320.00 - $425.00

Walther Model PPK/S (West German)
Same as Model PPK except: larger size to meet U.S.A. Treasury Dept. specifications in 1968; uses the slide & barrel of PPK Model mounted on the PP Model frame; add 4% for 22 long rifle
Estimated Value: $285.00 - $375.00

Walther Model PP Auto
Same as pre-World War II Model PP except: produced in West Germany; add 30% for 32 caliber; add 8% for 380 ACP
Estimated Value: $540.00 - $675.00

Walther Model PPK/S

Walther Model PPK

Walther Model PPK Auto
Same as pre-World War II Model PPK except produced in West Germany; importation into U.S.A. discontinued in 1968 due to restrictions imposed by the U.S. Treasury Dept.
Estimated Value: $400.00 - $500.00

Walther Model PPK Lightweight
Same as Model PPK except: aluminum alloy frame & not made in 380 caliber
Estimated Value: $340.00 - $450.00

Walther Model PPK American
Similar to the Model PPK except manufactured in the United States in blue or stainless steel
Estimated Value: $350.00 - $440.00

Semi-automatics

Walther Model P-5

Walther Model PPK/S American
Caliber: 380 ACP
Action: Semi-automatic; double action; exposed hammer
Magazine: 7-shot clip
Barrel: 3¼"
Finish: Blued or stainless steel; plastic grips; an American-built model of the Walther PPK/S
Estimated Value: $350.00 - $440.00

Walther Model P-5
Caliber: 9mm Parabellum
Action: Semi-automatic; double action; exposed hammer
Magazine: 8-shot clip
Barrel: 3½"
Finish: Blued; plastic grips; also Compact model with 3" barrel (add 30%)
Estimated Value: $740.00 - $ 925.00

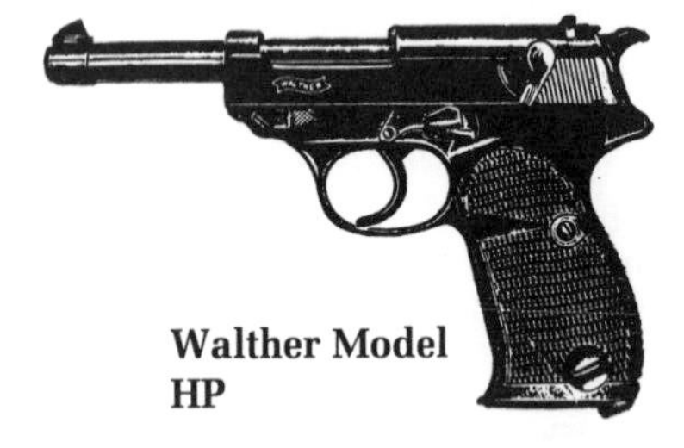

Walther Model HP

Walther Model HP
Caliber: 9mm Parabellum
Action: Semi-automatic; double action; exposed hammer
Magazine: 8-shot clip
Barrel: 5"
Finish: Blued; checkered walnut or plastic grips
Estimated Value: $760.00 - $950.00

Walther P-38 Military
Similar to Model HP except: modified version of the Model HP adopted as the Offical German service arm in 1938; a mass-produced military pistol; some of the wartime models were of very loose fit & very rough finish
Estimated Value: $400.00 - $500.00

Walther P-38

Walther P-38 (West German)
Same as P-38 Military Model except: improved workmanship; aluminum alloy frame; calibers 22 long rifle, 30 Luger & 9mm Parabellum; add 11% for 22 caliber
Estimated Value: $570.00 - $710.00

Walther Model P-38 IV

Walther Model P-38 IV
Similar to the P-38 (West German) with strengthened slide, no dust cover, & steel reinforced frame
Estimated Value: $415.00 - $520.00

Walther Model P-38 K
Similar to the Model P-38 IV with a 2¾" barrel
Estimated Value: $345.00 - $475.00

Walther Model TPH
Caliber: 22 long rifle, 25 ACP
Action: Semi-automatic, exposed hammer
Magazine: 6-shot clip, with finger rest
Barrel: 2¼"
Finish: Stainless steel; black plastic grips; a scaled-down version of the Model PP-PPK series in 22 long rifle & 25 ACP
Estimated Value: $265.00 - $335.00

Walther Model TPH

Walther Model P88

Walther Model P88
Caliber: 9mm Parabellum
Action: Double action, semi-automatic; exposed hammer
Magazine: 15-shot clip
Barrel: 4"
Finish: Blued, non reflective matte finish; alloy frame; black plastic grips
Estimated Value: $930.00 - $1,150.00

Webley

Webley 1906 Model Vest Pocket

Webley 1906 Model Vest Pocket
Caliber: 25 ACP
Action: Semi-automatic; exposed hammer; grip safety on front of grip
Magazine: 6-shot clip
Barrel: 2⅛"
Finish: Blued; checkered hard rubber grips
Estimated Value: $145.00 - $190.00

Webley & Scott 9mm Military & Police

Webley & Scott
1909 Model Vest Pocket
Similar to 1906 except: ejection port in top of slide; concealed hammer
Estimated Value: $175.00 - $220.00

Webley & Scott 9mm
Military & Police
Caliber: 9mm Browning long
Action: Semi-automatic; exposed hammer; grip safety
Magazine: 8-shot clip
Barrel: 5¼"
Finish: Blued; checkered plastic grips
Estimated Value: $375.00 - $500.00

Webley & Scott 1906 Model Police

Webley & Scott 1906 Model Police
Caliber: 32 ACP; 380 ACP
Action: Semi-automatic; exposed hammer; with or without grip safety
Magazine: 8-shot clip in 32 ACP, 7-shot clip in 380 ACP
Barrel: 3½"
Finish: Blued; checkered hard rubber grips
Estimated Value: $150.00 - $200.00

Webley & Scott Mark I No. 2
Similar to Mark I except: a slightly different version with fitted shoulder stock; issued to the British Royal Flying Corps in 1915; estimated value is for gun with shoulder stock
Estimated Value: $560.00 - $750.00

Webley & Scott Mark I
Caliber: 455 Webley self-loading
Action: Semi-automatic; exposed hammer; grip safety
Magazine: 7-shot clip
Barrel: 5"
Finish: Blued; checkered hard rubber or checkered walnut grips; adopted by British Royal Navy & Marines in 1913
Estimated Value: $285.00 - $360.00

Webley & Scott 38
Similar to Mark I except: a smaller modified version with concealed hammer; 8-shot magazine; 38 ACP caliber
Estimated Value: $225.00 - $300.00

Firearms Glossary

ACP - Automatic Colt Pistol. This abbreviation is used to denote ammunition designed for semi-automatic pistols

Action - The method by which a firearm is fed ammunition and fired; the portion of the firearm responsible for feeding ammunition, firing, and extracting fired cases

Adjustable choke - A muzzle attachment, either factory or manually installed, that allows the shooter to change the choke of his shotgun; several brands are available.

AE - Automatic ejector

Autoloading - Semi-automatic action; self loading; loads cartridges into chamber using the pressure of a fired cartridge

Automatic ejector - A device for extracting the fired case from the chamber when the action is opened

Automatic safety - A safety that is put into action by reloading or cocking the firearm

Barrel - The part of a gun through which the bullet or shot passes from breech to muzzle

Barrel adapter - A device inserted into a barrel to change the gauge or caliber to a smaller size

Barrel band - A metal ring encircling the barrel and forearm, found generally on carbines, lever actions, or full length forearms

Bead - A type of sight; a small round ball on top of the barrel at the muzzle

Beavertail - Wider than average

Blowback - A semi-automatic action, this operated by the pressure of the fired cartridge

Blueing - A finishing treatment applied to the metal portions of firearms for lasting protection; named for the blue-black final appearance; minimizes light reflection and protects against rust

Bolt action - An action, either repeating or single shot, that requires manual operation of the bolt handle to feed the chamber

Box lock - An action, with few working parts, found in break-open firearms

Box magazine - A box shaped magazine that stores and feeds the cartridges to the chamber

Breech - The rear end of the barrel where the chamber is located

Buck horn - A type of rear sight; the sides curve upward and inward over the open notch

Bull barrel - An unusually thick and heavy barrel

Butt plate - A sturdy piece attached to the rearmost section of the stock to protect the wood of the stock

Buttstock - The stock; the part of the gun extending from the receiver to the shooter's shoulder

Caliber - The diameter of the bore of a rifle or handgun

Carbine - A rifle with a short barrel, generally 16" to 20"

Case-hardened - A treatment, using carbon and extreme heat, for strengthening metal parts; the treated portion takes on a multi-colored, hazy finish

CB cap - A 22 caliber cartridge, shorter and less powerful than the 22 caliber short

CF (Centerfire) - A cartridge in which the primer is located in the center of the base or head

Chamber - The portion of the firearm that holds the cartridge during firing

Checkering - Patterned lines cut into the wood of grips, stocks, forearms, and slide handles; it is decorative and, at the same time, provides a non-slip surface

Cheekpiece - An extended area in the stock used for proper cheek positioning against the stock

Glossary

Choke - The design of a shotgun barrel that dictates the spread and pattern of shot leaving the barrel

Choke tube - A device that is inserted into the muzzle of a shotgun to alter the choke

Clip - A removable magazine, inserted into a firearm, that holds the cartridges and feeds them into the chamber

Comb - The upper portion of the stock

Compensator - A device attached to the muzzle or made into the barrel to reduce the upward swing of the barrel when fired

Cylinder - A rotating cartridge holder used in a revolver, in which the chambers are located

Damascus barrel - A type of barrel produced by welding small, twisted pieces of iron and steel in a spiral; these barrels were thought to be stronger in the late 1800's.

Derringer - Small, short, one or more barrelled handgun, easily concealed

Double action (DA) - Designation of a handgun that can be discharged simply by pulling the trigger; manual cocking is unnecessary

Double barrel - A gun with two barrels, usually a shotgun, rifle, or rifle/shotgun combination with barrels side-by-side or over-and-under

Double set trigger - A device with two triggers; one sets a spring mechanism to assist the firing trigger; usually found on target guns

Dovetail - A groove by which the sight is attached to the barrel

Ejector - A mechanism for removing, or partially removing, empty cases from the gun

Exposed hammer - A visible hammer that can be manually cocked

Extractor - A device that draws the cartridge or empty case from the chamber when the action is opened

Falling block - An action, found in some early single shots, in which the chamber closing mechanism moves vertically by moving a lever

Firing Pin - The device that strikes the primer part of a cartridge to fire the cartridges

Finish - The exterior appearance of a gun including type of wood, stock, forearm, and type of metal, sights, decoration, and added features

Fixed sights - Stationary sights; not movable

Flash supressor - An instrument that reduces or hides muzzle flame or flash

Fluted - A shallow groove or grooves found on some forearms and on revolver cylinders

Forearm - The portion of the gun under the barrel that is gripped when firing; usually made of wood; the forearm can be in the form of a slide handle on slide action gun

Front sight - The sight at the muzzle end of the barrel

Gas operation - A type of action in which gas from a discharging cartridge is used to operate the action

Gauge - The bore size of a shotgun

Grip safety - A safety device located on the grip of a pistol; the shooter's hand releases the safety as it grips the pistol to fire

Hammer - A spring powered piece that strikes the firing pin; it is actuated by the trigger

Hammerless - A gun with a concealed hammer or striking mechanism

Handgun - A gun that is operated with one hand; revolver, single shot, or semi-automatic pistol

Handguard - A piece that fits on top of the barrel to protect the hand from the heat of rapid fire; usually found on military type rifles

Hooded sight - A sight with a protective cover

Lanyard loop or ring - A metal ring on military handguns that is attached to a strap

Lever action - A firearm in which the action is operated by the movement of a lever, usually part of the trigger guard

Loading gate - In revolvers, a piece that swings open to allow loading; in long guns, a spring powered door that is forced open when loading cartridges into the magazine

Long - The middle designation of a 22 caliber cartridge, longer than a short, shorter than a long rifle

Long rifle - The designation of a 22 caliber cartridge more powerful than a long

Magazine - The portion of the gun that holds cartridges ready for feeding into the chamber; in repeating weapons only

Magnum - A more powerful cartridge than the standard cartridge of the same caliber

Mannlicher stock - A one-piece stock and forearm that extends the length of the barrel

Micrometer - A highly accurate adjustable sight found mainly on target rifles or pistols

Monte Carlo - A type of stock in which there is a rise at the forward portion; usually has a cheek piece

Muzzle - Forward end of the barrel

Open sight - A "notched" sight

Palm rest - An adjustable handgrip found on match rifles

Parkerizing - A matte, rust resistant surface applied to metal with a phosphate solution; used on military firearms

Patridge sights - A square notched rear sight and square post front sight

Peep sight - A circular rear sight with a small hole that provides greater accuracy than open or notched sights

Pistol - Handgun; usually a semi-automatic handgun

Pistol grip - The grip portion of a handgun; or a grip resembling that of a pistol built into the stock of a shotgun or rifle

Pump - Slide action

Ramp sight - A front sight that is positioned atop a ramp base

Recoil pad - A rubber cushion attached to some shotguns and high powered rifles designed to reduce recoil impact on the shooter

Rem - Remington

Repeating - Any rifle or shotgun that has a magazine and may be fired without reloading after each shot

Revolver - A handgun that uses a rotating cylinder to hold and fire cartridges

Rib - A flat piece fitted on top of the barrel to aid in sighting or add decor; may be ventilated, matte, or solid

RF (Rimfire) - A cartridge in which the firing primer is in the perimeter of the shell base or head

SAA - Single Action Army

Safety - A mechanism that prevents the gun from being fired

Schnabel - A decorative lip at the end of a forearm

Semi-automatic - An autoloading action in which cartridges are fed automatically; the trigger must be pressed for every desired discharge

Short - A small 22 caliber cartridge

Shotgun - A non-rifled long gun, designated by gauge, for firing shot shells

Side lever - A lever located on the side of a receiver that is tripped to open the gun

Single action - The hammer must be cocked before the gun can be fired

Single set trigger - A trigger that can be fired by heavy pull or put into another position to allow light pull

Single trigger - A single trigger used to fire a double barrel shotgun; a selective single trigger is equipped with a lever that allows the shooter to choose the barrel to be discharged first; the non-selective trigger is always fired in the same, factory-set sequence

Slide action - A pump action long arm. An action that requires a manual slide of the forearm section (slide handle) in order to complete the action cycle

Sling - A removable strap usually attached to military, high powered hunting and some target rifles or shotguns

Glossary

Snubnose - A revolver with a very short barrel

Spec. (Special) - Usually to denote ammunition (as 38 Special)

S&W - Smith & Wesson

Swivel - A metal loop through which is passed a sling for carrying; either detachable or stationary

Takedown - A gun that can be easily taken apart for transport or storage

TD - Takedown

Thumbhole - A feature found mostly on match rifles, a hole in the stock for the shooter's thumb

Thumb lever - A lever atop the frame that is tripped to break open the firearm

Thumb rest - Usually found on handgun grips, a place to rest the thumb to provide better hold

Trigger - The piece under the action that is pressed to open the firing mechanism

Trigger guard - A metal barrier around the trigger for protection of the trigger

Tubular magazine - A tube in which cartridges are stored end to end, ready to be transported to the chamber; can be under barrel or in stock

UMC - Union Metallic Cartridge Co.

Ventilated rib - A rib that is separated from the barrel by short posts

Win. - Winchester

WMR - Winchester Magnum Rim Fire

WRA - Winchester Repeating Arms Company